A Free-Range Dog
by
Tovey Brooke

Tovey with 'Her' (otherwise Betty Brooke)

A FREE-RANGE DOG
by
TOVEY BROOKE

Translated by Betty Brooke

Illustrated by Al Thomas

First published in 1990 by
Arthur James Limited
One Cranbourne Road, London N10 2BT

British Library Cataloguing in Publication Data
Brooke, Tovey
  A free-range dog.
  I. Title   II. Brooke, Betty
  828.91409
  ISBN 0-85305-294-8

Typesetting and artwork by Stumptype, London

Printed by The Guernsey Press Co. Ltd., Guernsey, Channel Islands

Dedicated
To all people who love dogs
and to all dogs who love people

Illustrations and Cover Design by Al Thomas

TOVEY

Tovey Brooke was born in Guernsey. His birth date is unknown and there is, of course, no record of him in the Kennel Club. His escapades have been highlighted in the articles which his owner contributes to the *Jersey Evening Post*. Two books containing selections from these articles have already been published so that Tovey is now known outside the limits of the Channel Islands. This is his first published work.

Betty Brooke, with whom Tovey now lives in Jersey, is almost as well-known as her dog with the Queen Anne feet. For twenty years a political columnist and now a Senator in Jersey's Parliament, she has made her mark as a writer, broadcaster and lay preacher. Her love of life and laughter gurgle up from some inexhaustible spring.

Al Thomas, who has drawn the illustrations for Tovey's book, is a graphic artist. His cartoons and drawings have been developed to a high standard and the originals are much sought after by those who recognise the quality of his work.

Contents

Chapter One

EARLY DAYS

I am a Channel Island dog. I was born in Guernsey, I now live in Jersey and I once went to Sark for the weekend. Behind that somewhat stark announcement there is a wealth of experience of the world from a dog's point of view.

I am not an ordinary dog. I may look like an ordinary dog, but much of what has happened to me during my life has been extra-ordinary. I have not courted trouble or adventures but, for some reason, trouble has constantly pursued me and adventures have been thrust upon me. She said to me one day that She could write a book about my misdeeds. So far She has failed to do this so *I* am setting pen to paper, or rather paw to keyboard, and writing my own life story.

I ought to explain that She is the person with whom I have lived for the last seven years. We are now, She says, sharing our declining years. That is a fanciful notion, but then She has such notions. What is more She tells me at regular intervals that I have shortened her life because of the worry I have caused her. Be that as it may, our declining years are not noticeably any different from the ones which went before them. She still reaches for *The Times* to give me a well-deserved whack and her wrist has not lost its strength; nor have I lost my speed when it comes to avoiding the onset of the daily news.

Many people write their life stories. Some are famous, some are infamous and some just jump on to the bandwagon in the hope that the book will make them a fortune. I have no desire for money — although She could use a little owing to the vast amount of money which has been spent on fencing because of me. The cost of keeping me at home has been enormous and if we recouped just that sum, I suppose She would be pleased. All *I* seek to achieve is to explain how, despite evidence produced to the contrary, I have been generally the innocent victim of circumstances beyond my control. Life stories begin with one's early life. I was born in Guernsey. My mother was a black flat-coated retriever called Sophy who had been a Cruft's winner. She came to Guernsey as a tax exile, or to be more accurate I should say that the people who brought her to the island were tax exiles.

Sophy may have been a Cruft's winner but she had a wandering eye and her morals left a great deal to be desired. I sometimes think that dogs are rather like people. Some of the best-bred people get up to the most extraordinary things, if one believes the gossip columnists. Breeding seems to make little difference, and some well-pedigreed people, like Sophy, have no moral sense at all.

It had been the Tax Exiles' intention to breed little flat-coated black retrievers like Sophy but my Mum had other ideas. One night she got out of Fort William where the Tax Exiles had a rather luxurious pad, and I was the result of her night of passion. Looking at me one could only imagine what sort of a chap my Dad must have been. Certainly my appearance had quite an effect on the TEs. Sophy told me they took one look at me and said in chorus, "Oh my God", which Sophy felt showed they must have had some faith in prayer. One look at me had made them appeal to the Almighty for support.

I am, in fact, a fairly normal looking dog. I have Sophy's black shiny coat. My feet are pure Queen Anne and, like the clock at Grantchester, stand permanently at Ten-to-Three. I learned about the Grantchester clock from my declining years' companion. She did once say that, if I were a piece of furniture, with my feet I would be very valuable. She also pointed out to a friend that, although I had distinguished feet, I had a very common tail. I suppose my curled tail is a bit of a disaster, and it may have been the combination of the feet and the tail which made the Tax Exiles resort to prayer when they saw what Sophy had produced.

Although they may have had a belief in the power of prayer, they did not have hearts of gold for, when I was about six months old, they decided that I should be advertised for sale in the local paper. I was by then already showing the free-range symptoms which are part of my character. Free-range is a disease which attacks animals and humans. Sophy told me that men are natural free-rangers and some wives have a dreadful time trying to keep free-range husbands in check.

My first attempt to escape from the Fort William prison was unsuccessful. They found the tunnel which I had constructed with such care as a permanent line of escape. It had taken me a long time to dig it under the rose bed and when the gardener filled it in, I realised that my days with the TEs were numbered.

The newspaper advertisement was the direct result of the tunnel incident and when they discussed, in my hearing, the possibility of me being sold, I was touched by the female TE's concern.

"A prospective buyer is bound to want him and give him a good home," she said. "He has rather endearing brown eyes." The male of the species snorted loudly and lighted a brown tube in his face. It gave off the most extraordinary smell. I think he must have been frightened that a bloodhound from the Tax Office would pick up his scent!

The next few days were very fraught for me because I realised that my whole future depended on the sort of prospective buyer who would come along. Sadly, only one appeared which meant there was very little choice when it came to finding me 'a good home'.

The Prospective Buyer, hereinafter known as the PB, decided very quickly

that she would have me because she had children who wanted a dog. That is, may I say, the very worst reason for acquiring one. The Tax Exiles were delighted, but Sophy took me on one side and said the PB was not the sort of person whom she would have chosen for her son.

"Where's her husband?" she muttered. "Looks the sort of bitch who would live fast and loose." Coming from Sophy I must own that was pretty rich. Sophy would have made an excellent heroine for a canine soap opera. She had marvellous looks and she was quite promiscuous. I believe that, after I left, she found a wandering Basset Hound for whom she developed an undying passion and they drove the Tax Exiles nearly mad singing love songs nightly to the moon.

I was very sorry to leave Sophy although I did not cast a backward glance at the Tax Exiles. They had very little breeding although, according to Sophy, they had lived in a Manor House in the Home Counties in England. I am not too sure where the Home Counties are, but I gathered from Sophy that they were not islands and therefore not worthy of my attention. However, I found the PB's bijou residence something of a culture shock after Fort William.

The PB lived with a litter of children who were a pain in the neck to me. At first, when I was a novelty, they were fairly gentle with me but, when I grew bigger, they used to ride me round the garden one at a time until I was literally down to my knees. The afternoons in the garden were a disaster. The PB would occasionally intervene, but, on the whole, she viewed their behaviour with a tolerance which I found unacceptable so I decided that the time had come for me to seek fresh fields and pastures new. By then I was about nine months old and more or less fully grown. It is a pity that humans have not trained dogs to race like horses. I know that a greyhound will chase an imitation rabbit round a racetrack because, of course, greyhounds have not got a lot between the ears. Any dog with even a modicum of intelligence would know that an imitation rabbit is not worth chasing. What is not realised is that dogs like me could enter races like the Grand National. I can leap almost any fence or gate and the PB's gate was puppy play to me. I chose a time when she was giving the litter their supper and I leapt the gate to set off on my life of dissipation.

Chapter Two

A PUB DOG

It was on my very first night of freedom that I became a pub dog, and turned into what She laughingly calls her Guernsey alcoholic.

I think, in fairness to me, it must be said that I did not set out to become an alcoholic. I merely went into the warmth of the pub in St Peter Port because I was cold and hungry. At that moment I was beginning to feel that even the PB's neglect was better than wandering about alone in the cold. The pub I chose was full of people and I slipped under a chair to rest for a little while before seeing if there was any food about.

"There's a dog under your chair," a man said to his friend who was sitting opposite to him at the table.

"Pull the other one, Charlie" said a voice above me which I realised was some sort of Guernsey repartee which might or might not be a prelude to an offer of friendship.

"There is a dog under your chair. He's got funny black feet and one ear sticks up higher than the other," said the man whose powers of observation would have earned him a chance to go off and train as a police dog if he could have found a Handler.

"One of *your* ears sticks up more than the other, Charlie," said the man above me in a funny slurred voice. At that point I decided to try to advance my cause with a genuine offer of friendship. I crawled out from under his chair and put my head lovingly on his knee. "Oh my God," he said weakly, so I bowed my head and closed my eyes as the PB's children had taught me. They used to pray every night which, I suppose, was just as well with the PB as a mother. The praying trick always earned me half a biscuit at the very least. The man did not reach for a biscuit but said, in a strangled voice, "I think he's dead." Now 'dead' was a trick I did particularly well, so I crashed to the floor and rolled over with my paws in the air, shutting my eyes at the same time. The trick had an astonishing effect on the man. He staggered to his feet and rushed out of the pub. A small crowd gathered round me and Charlie said weakly, "Do you think we should give him the kiss of life?" I must say what happened next was a great surprise to me. The man Charlie bent down and started to blow up my nose. I shot to my feet and began to catch my tail — a trick I had perfected during the weeks I spent with the children. Everyone in the pub began to clap.

One man dressed in a guernsey and blue trousers (which most Guernseymen wear when they go to sea or work in the fields) patted my head and said, "Buy him a drink, Charlie".

There was a burst of laughter and the next thing I knew was that a glass of brown liquid was placed in front of me. It was my first taste of beer and I have to admit it went down a treat. Then someone gave me a packet of crisps and they watched me opening it with admiration. I can open a packet of crisps quicker than most people can say 'Guernsey tomatoes'. The PB's children were fairly quick on the draw and I had become very adept at stealing their crisps and eating them before they discovered I had the packet. Mostly we lived on coke, crisps and baked beans. The Tax Exiles never had anything like that. They gave Sophy special dog food which she had apparently advertised when she won the Top Award at Crufts. I didn't think much of it, but then I was never a top dog which probably had something to do with it. The Tax Exiles ate steaks and beef and lobsters and complained loudly if things were not properly cooked. They would have been better to try them raw. Cooking spoils food. I was thinking of steaks and lobsters and I suddenly found that I had a lump in my throat remembering Sophy and how the Tax Exiles, with all their faults, always remembered our dinner.

"That dog's hungry," a woman behind the bar said. "I'll get him some sausage rolls." I don't think anything has ever tasted as good as those three sausage rolls in that pub on my first night of freedom. Food had not been in plentiful supply at the Prospective Buyer's and I was often hungry, but that night when I slipped out of the pub I had a warm glow inside me and two packets of crisps, three sausage rolls and a quarter of bitter. Outside it was dark and I slipped down to the harbour where I knew I would be able to find somewhere to sleep. I found a pile of lobster pots covered by a tarpaulin and I crawled under it, curled up and wondered if the PB was out calling for me in the little lane where her cottage, appropriately named the Love Nest, was situated.

It was my first experience of being completely alone and I enjoyed it. The PB's children seldom gave me a whole night's sleep because they were either teething or getting up to lift their legs and they preceded both these operations with howls of distress in the middle of the night. Under the tarpaulin there was perfect peace and the sound of the water lapping against the jetty lulled me to sleep. It was the first time I had felt happy since I left Sophy.

Chapter Three

GEORGE AND DORIS

St Peter Port soon became very familiar to me. I used to meet the mail boat and watch the people coming ashore. Sometimes they looked a pale shade of green and seemed unsteady on their feet, and I used to wonder what happened on the journey. The same could be said for passengers coming off the Hydrofoils which go between the islands and St Malo. I have overheard wives clinging to their husbands and saying "Never again" and phrases like that. I remember one couple in particular who came off the St Malo Hydrofoil and both looked extremely groggy. I went up to them to give them a sort of welcome-to-Guernsey tail-wag which I had perfected over the months of wandering; it was usually good for a biscuit, but on this occasion it was a disaster. "Look at that dog's feet, George," the woman said weakly. "They're at right angles to his body, and he's got one ear up and the other down. I've never seen such a dog." "Try not to look at him, dear, and he may go away," her husband said briskly. I must say I was deeply offended by their remarks, and decided there and then that I would win them over by my constant companionship. Humans make extraordinarily hurtful personal remarks about us dogs, I find. I could have told her that her hair needed touching up because the blonde bits were growing out and that she was distinctly overweight, but I simply would not have dreamed of making such derogatory remarks even if I could have spoken their language. As for George suggesting that I might go away — well, that strengthened my determination to stay with them and win them over. They presented a distinct challenge. They had a ten-day holiday in Guernsey and I never left them alone for a single moment. Well, that is of course a slight exaggeration for I did not actually sleep in their bedroom, but I waited outside their hotel each night and was there to greet them in the morning. I went to meet Charlie most nights in the pub when they had gone to bed and had my usual half-pint with the boys, but otherwise I devoted my daylight hours to George and Doris. It was a lovely ten days for me but I thought, once or twice, that they found my constant devotion an embarrassment.

I remember on about the fifth day she said to him,

"George, do you think that dog has no home?" George looked at me and said sadly, "Nobody would give a dog who looked like that a home." I thought that this was a little hurtful but it strengthened my determination to stay with them to the end of their holiday. I would have liked to have explained that I did indeed have a home but frankly it was not up to much and I preferred living the life of a vagrant. I suppose I am really a tramp dog by nature although She has more or less ensured that my roving days are done. I heard her telling a friend the other day that the fencing has cost her nearly eight hundred pounds which seems to me to be a great deal of money which could have been better employed buying bones and biscuits.

To get back to George and Doris; they began to look for me when they came out of their hotel and once, when I had gone round the corner to see if Charlie

15

was in the paper shop, they got quite worked up because I wasn't outside as usual. I was wandering back to the hotel when I heard George whistling and Doris calling "Come here". They didn't know my name so several other dogs appeared but I soon saw them off — although for a few moments George and Doris looked as if they were rounding up stray dogs for the Shelter. To my surprise Doris bent down and gave me a piece of bacon which she had obviously stolen from the dining room. "It's our last day, George," she said apologetically, "and I'm going to miss him." Her eyes filled with tears and George put his arm round her.

"We can't take him with us, darling," he said with a tenderness I would not have thought him capable of ten days ago.

"Please, George," she said. I stood rooted to the spot. I had overdone the devotion act and now my whole way of life was under threat. What would Charlie and the boys say if I was not at the pub that evening because I would be *en route* for Welwyn Garden City (about which I had heard much while wandering behind them over the cliffs)? It sounded a very odd place to me, and George and Doris seemed to lead a very strange life. They never mentioned going to the pub, for they were obviously much too busy Morris Dancing. I had never heard of the activity until I met them. They had joined up on one of our walks with some other people from the hotel and they had told this other couple of their Morris Dancing club. It sounded distinctly odd to me, all that leaping about, knocking sticks and bladders. In fact it sounded a most sadistic activity to which someone called Morris had lent his name. I could see a life stretching before me of exciting afternoons at charity fêtes in Welwyn Garden City and its environs, with George and Doris dancing and me tied up to a lamp post watching them.

"Please, George," she said again. He looked at me and I could see he was weakening. He bent down and I licked his hand. He didn't know it was a farewell kiss.

"He likes you, George," she said ingratiatingly. I wagged my tail and stood up on my back legs and let her ruffle the hair on top of my head — a practice which I actually dislike intensely. At that moment Charlie came round the corner with his paper. I turned on my paws and chased after him. It was the end of my relationship with George and Doris. They left that night on the boat. I watched them go from under a coach which I occasionally used when I was hiding from the police. It was nice to feel wanted — and not by the police, who seemed always intent upon catching me — but Welwyn Garden City and the Morris dancing just did not seem to be my scene.

Chapter Four

ENCOUNTERS WITH THE POLICE

Having mentioned being "wanted by the police", I ought perhaps to explain that I had a very close relationship with those responsible for law and order during my free-range days. I do not think it is an exaggeration to state that policemen, on the whole, do not like either free-range people or free-range dogs. They call free-range people 'tramps', and free-range dogs 'strays'. Tramps and strays present a challenge to a policeman which he finds hard to resist. One Spring afternoon when I had been missing from the PB's desirable residence for some weeks, I was examining a dustbin down a small alleyway when a police car drew up alongside me. The window was wound down, and a Plod with a red face shouted "Oy, you!". Now I am, by nature, a friendly dog and answer to almost any name, so I ambled over to the car and the Plod got out. I wagged my tail hoping that he was going to give me a Plod biscuit from the pocket of his uniform. This, I quickly realised, was not his intention at all and, before I could draw breath, he had grabbed me by the collar, picked me up and thrown me into the back of the car where another Plod was sitting. I landed on top of Plod Two, winding him totally and causing him to drop the ham sandwich which he was apparently consuming during his short break. I caught the ham sandwich before it reached the floor of the car and ate it hastily.

"The perishing dog's pinched my sandwich," Plod Two said indignantly. "Why didn't you warn me what you were going to do? Having a black dog land on one's stomach while eating a sandwich is enough to give anyone a proper turn." "Oh, give over," said Plod One. "You think too much about food. See if he's got a name on his collar." The gutsy Plod leaned down and examined my collar. I licked his hand because I felt that he and I would have had quite a bit in common if we had time to get to know each other.

"No name, and probably no licence either," he said gloomily.

At the mention of the word 'licence' my heart sank. Licences are very important things. Charlie had his licence taken away and it meant he could not drive a car. The PB had her television taken away because They discovered that she didn't have a licence for it. Mabel, who ran the *First and Last*, the pub where I had spent so many happy hours with the boys, lived in daily fear of having her licence taken away. Every Saturday night, when there was a fight in the Public Bar, she used to bang on the counter and yell, "What'll you lot do if I lose my licence?" It always had a most calming effect and those who had been intent upon proving that Jocks were better than Scouses postponed the battle for another night. So I had long ago realised that licences were extremely important. What I had not realised until that moment in the Plods' car was that, just as Charlie needed a licence to drive a car and the PB had to have a licence to watch her television and Mabel had to have a licence to run her pub, so someone had to have a licence to have me! It was a Black Moment, and just then Plod Two said thoughtfully "I think I've seen this dog at the *First and Last*".

"You spend too much time in pubs in your off-duty," said Plod One briskly.

"There's more to life than eating and drinking, you know." I jumped up on the seat and put my paw on the Plod's knee. I had found a soul mate. He looked surprised by my obvious devotion. I suppose policemen on the whole do not evoke that sort of emotion in those whom they apprehend.

"We'll go round and call on Mabel," Plod One said, switching on the car's engine.

As the car slid forward, I wished I could have told them that I get sick in cars. I think it is to do with the smell. The Tax Exiles' Rolls Royce always had a rich aroma of leather and perfume. The Female Tax Exile had some very expensive stuff she used to mask her scent. I used to get into the Rolls and almost immediately I would heave. The Tax Exiles gave up taking me in the end after one or two rather embarrassing rides.

The PB had a very small Citroen which smelled of cheese and onion. This was because the children were addicted to cheese and onion crisps. I preferred the bacon flavoured ones, but beggars can't be choosers so I would tuck into the cheese and onion ones with a will. I suppose that, over the months, the constant fighting over the packets meant that a certain proportion of the crisps got trampled into the rubber mats and some went down the car seats. I could smell that car a mile away and, if I had been asked to find it in a Deux Cheveux rally of a thousand cars in the Bois de Boulogne in Paris, I could have sniffed it out in two seconds flat.

The police car did not smell of leather, perfume or cheese and onion. It reminded me of the flea powder the gardener at Fort William applied to me when I had had a close encounter with a hedgehog who, apparently, had not bathed for some time. The Plods' car must have been de-loused at some point because it had that familiar pong.

We had only travelled for a few minutes before I felt my familiar car sickness coming over me. My stomach began to heave. Plod Two panicked.

"He's going to be sick, Bob, stop the car." Plod One, whose name was apparently Bob, acted swiftly. Without glancing in his mirror, he stood on his brakes and there was an almighty crash. It seemed to me that someone in a car behind was intent on joining our happy little threesome. Plod Two appeared to be dazed but unhurt. He opened the door and I reached the gutter just in time. A red-faced man emerged from the dark blue Jaguar which had somehow mounted our police car from the rear. I could tell, at a glance, that he was a person of some importance and I could also sense that he was not pleased. I felt that it was an appropriate moment for me to leave my new-found Plod friends. I slipped between the two cars and made good my escape up a small lane which I knew led to a building site where Charlie's friend, Jack, worked. I lay low for a while under the Portacabin on the site and that night, in the pub, I heard the sequel to my adventure. The man in the Jaguar was the Top Plod and he had not been over-impressed by Plod Bob's unsignalled, unscheduled stop in the street.

"Apparently, the police had arrested a stray dog and their story was that he had bitten the driver which had caused him to brake suddenly," Mabel said.

"The lying Plod," I muttered under my chair. "You should expect absolute

honesty from the men in blue." "What's Tovey growling for?" said Mabel to
Charlie. At that moment the door swung open and standing about five paws'
length away from my nose were two pairs of black, highly polished shoes. I
sniffed and noted a faint trace of flea powder perfume.

"Out you come," said a Ploddish voice, and before you could say 'Guernsey
tomatoes' I found myself in an iron grip and deposited in what seemed to me to
be a fortress on wheels heading for the Dog Prison. Later that night, as I
examined my cell, I wondered if they would find my licence and release me, or if
I would have to work out a method of tunnelling my way to freedom.

Chapter Five

A TASTE FOR GOLF

When I woke up on my first morning of captivity, I was pleasantly surprised by
the high standard of my prison. We had individual cells which is more than can
be said for the conditions under which human prisoners live. I gather there is
dreadful over-crowding amongst the human prison population, but we were in
solitary confinement with a very pleasant outdoor run. The people who ran the
Shelter were extremely civil and, furthermore, they had the right idea about the
need to feed us at regular intervals. The food was good and plentiful, although a
pampered Pekinese made a great song and dance about his rations which

apparently did not suit the Chinese gentleman. I gathered that he was a boarder and a casualty of the package holiday business. The growth of the package holiday business has played absolute havoc with the lives of us dogs. At one time owners were quite content to have just a once-a-year holiday but since package holidays became popular, dogs are so often put into boarding kennels that they become quite insecure. The Chinese gentleman was a typical example of boarding-house blues. He would not eat, barked half the night and yapped half the day.

The Shelter had its share of boarders, and strays like Rusty and me whose free-range tendencies were a challenge to authority. I was glad to see Rusty in the next cell because we had met up once or twice on our wanderings and I owed my life to him when I was set upon unexpectedly by a Boxer dog. Generally speaking I could look after myself very well and, being a pacifist by nature, I was not usually involved in any street brawls. On the occasion when I encountered the punch-drunk Boxer, I had been minding my own business, quietly chewing a bone which the butcher had given me. The bone was not stolen, it did not belong to the Boxer, I had come by it honestly and I was, therefore, somewhat aggrieved when this huge chap with the turned-up nose pounced on me. I dropped the bone hastily but that did not appease him for he pinned me to the ground and I felt that perhaps my last moment had come.

A small crowd gathered round but no one tried to pull him off me. One woman began to scream.

"Help, help, he's going to kill him," she cried, confirming what I had been thinking. At that moment Rusty appeared like an avenging angel (whatever that might be; I have heard them referred to so I know they do exist). Rusty is not a big dog, being a cross between a fox terrier and a West Highland, but his reputation as a street-fighter is considerable. He launched himself at the Boxer

like an Exocet missile and I felt the impact as my assailant turned on my rescuer. I thought that I ought to lend a hand so I attacked from underneath and Rusty got hold of one of his ears. The Boxer shook his head and Rusty was projected through the air, knocking down the woman who had been having a hysterical fit over the fracas.

"Get him," she yelled in a most blood-thirsty manner from her prone position on the ground. Rusty staggered to his feet and returned to the fray. I had been holding on like grim death so was glad to have Rusty's continued support. Eventually the Boxer, realising he was beaten, made off. Rusty then grinned at me and took my bone and, although it had been particularly juicy one, I felt he deserved it. In any case he was not the sort of chap with whom one argued over a bone.

We had met once or twice after that incident and on one occasion he persuaded me to go with him to watch a golf match. Rusty was a golf addict and spent a lot of time on *L'Ancresse Common* where people who were besotted with the notion of hitting a small ball and then following it, only to hit it again, were to be found. Rusty arranged to meet me at the first tee where he assured me we would receive a warm welcome from the lady captain of the opposing team. If Rusty's idea of a warm welcome was to be chased across the common by some wild women brandishing golf clubs, then he has a psychological problem which he is going to have to address one day. They have, incidentally, very good dog shrinks nowadays who could cope with Rusty — and might have a quick look at the Peke too, come to think of it.

We escaped from our pursuers and he showed me where there was a very pleasant large hole filled with warm sand. We lay down in it, panting, when suddenly a small object like a seagull's egg hit me smack between the eyes. Rusty picked it up and disappeared over the horizon while I lay trying desperately to stop the world spinning past me. The next moment a mad woman appeared, looking down at me from the top of the sandpit.

"Where's my ball?" she shrieked, brandishing her club in a most threatening manner. She had taken the club from a bag which she had attached to a sort of pushchair. Her opponent then appeared and she was a very frightening sight. She wore a windcheater and trousers and, as she was very fat, she looked for all the world to me, in my dazed condition, like 'Michelin man'.

"You can play another ball from where you think it landed," she grunted tersely — giving, as I later discovered, a totally wrong ruling. "If you think that dog's swallowed it, you could perhaps tee up on his stomach." At that point I decided that lady golfers were a very special breed and, like Boxers, to be avoided at all costs. I pulled myself together, scrambled up the opposite side of the sandpit and legged it in roughly the direction I thought Rusty had taken.

I found him down in a little cove on the beach and he took me into his secret hideout behind an old German occupation fortification. I should think he had over a hundred golf balls there, in various stages of destruction. He had an insatiable appetite for them and he offered me one to chew to compensate for the bump on the head. I gave it a perfunctory lick or two but golf balls, like avocado pears, are an acquired taste. Rusty, on the other hand, felt a day was wasted if he had not retrieved one golf ball for his own use — which just goes to show that tastes are different. He told me that when it came to beer he could take it or leave it, which may have been sour grapes on his part because I doubt if anyone had ever bought him a half-pint. His golf ball obsession certainly taught me that we all have our own particular addictions.

Rusty had apparently done several stints in the Shelter because his owner refused to pay to get him out. He was, therefore, available for adoption and he used to sit waiting hopefully for a Prospective Adopter to come along. My own position was less clear for I gathered from the conversation which I overheard that the PB had been contacted and might well come and bail me out.

The next day a Prospective Adopter appeared and I heard a voice which I instantly recognised. It was an extraordinary coincidence!

"I would like a good obedient dog as a companion. I will take him back to Alderney with me," said the familiar voice. Alderney is an adjacent island where Charlie and his mates occasionally go for what they call 'a Norgy'. I am not sure what 'a Norgy' is, but it sounds the sort of exercise that means a hangover the next day. Anyway the lady from Alderney whose voice I recognised hove in sight.

"Good heavens," she said, looking into my cell. "That's the dog who ate my golf ball and it cost me the championship. I wouldn't have him as a gift."

She moved down the line and stopped at Rusty's quarters. Rusty wagged his tail beguilingly and to my astonishment I heard her say, "He looks a good, reliable dog, I'll take him."

Rusty smirked as he was led out but I felt that his might be a short-term adoption. I was right. He was back the next morning and I gathered from Dora, the kennel maid, that he had been far from an unqualified success. She told Sam, one of her colleagues, about Rusty's short relationship with his Prospective Adopter. "She left him in her hotel bedroom last night. She was due to fly back to Alderney this afternoon. Apparently her golf clubs were propped up in the bathroom and the ball-pocket was open. He chewed up fifteen balls during the course of the night and he wouldn't let her into the bathroom this morning. The hotel proprietor sent for the police and Rusty was quite happy to let them in. They gathered up the chewed balls and I've put them in with Rusty," said Dora in explanation.

Rusty lined the balls up in his exercise yard and lay looking at them in a thoroughly besotted way. His adoption might not have worked out, but his return to captivity was certainly made more tolerable by his golf ball haul.

Chapter Six

THE RESCUE

After Rusty's abortive adoption, there seemed to be very little excitement in the Shelter. Although I knew that the authorities had been in touch with the PB, I didn't know if she was going to come along and get me out. I was missing Charlie and the pub gang and, to be honest, a drop of beer would have gone down very nicely with the evening rations. I knew Charlie would adopt me if he could, but Mrs Charlie was the fly in the ointment. She was 'allergic-to-dogs' according to him and she had told him that if he brought me home, she would go! "Mind you, I'm tempted to take her upon that," Charlie said one night in the *First and Last* when he was talking about my homeless state. "She won't come out with me of an evening, but Tovey is always game for a pint."

I thought of the conversation as I lay watching Rusty consuming yet another golf ball, but I must own that I thought that line of escape was pretty slender. Four days after Rusty's hotel bathroom escapade I heard a familiar sound. It was the unmistakable noise of a Deux Cheveux Citroen badly in need of servicing. A few minutes later the PB and the twins Andrewanmark appeared. When I first met the PB's litter, I could not work out how many children she had, and furthermore there was a pair who might as well have been Siamese twins because they were constantly together and totally indistinguishable. They were known as Andrewanmark. The PB swept into the Shelter in her usual high-handed manner and demanded my instant release. Andrewanmark appeared outside the cells and, spotting Rusty, began to shout in unison.

"Let's have him, Mummy," which I must own was somewhat disconcerting. The PB was not to be put off and after the financial arrangements were settled, she marched me out and put me into the car where I was instantly overwhelmed by the smell of cheese and onion.

It was fortunately a short journey to the Love Nest and, as the PB was muttering throughout the journey about the way Andrewanmark were behaving and about the ingratitude of dogs and of my infidelity, I was distracted enough to keep my breakfast down.

The Love Nest was as chaotic as ever and the three older children, on their return from school, gave me an enthusiastic welcome home. There was no garden attached to the Love Nest and the backyard was positively awash with tricycles, wheelbarrows, skateboards and the PB's pottery impedimenta. She had decided to take up pottery just before my arrival from the Tax Exiles and, if her first efforts were anything to go by, famous potters, like Leach, had nothing to fear in the way of a new competitor.

The bowl on which she was working when I first arrived was so lop-sided that she decided it would do as my water-dish. Drinking out of it demanded a very special skill because the bowl tipped over if the slightest pressure were exerted and I spent many thirsty hours waiting for a refill. There were few improvements to the property since my departure although she had put some trellis fencing on top of the gate as a security device, which she pointed out to me.

"That'll stop you getting up to your tricks," she said proudly, and I viewed the challenge with interest. I had no intention of staying with the PB for a day longer than necessary, for it was not the sort of environment which suited me. I was a street dog by nature and being confined in a backyard when the family went out was so claustrophobic that I, literally, felt like 'climbing the walls'. I thought for all our sakes I should leave quite quickly in case the enforced captivity would be harmful to my character — added to which, I was longing for a half-pint with Charlie and the boys.

On the first evening of my return to the Love Nest I was put out while the PB gave the litter their supper, as was the custom there, and, without a backward glance, I shinned up the gate, wriggled through the trellis fencing and set off for the *First and Last*. Halfway down the dark road I saw a bundle of what I took to be clothes lying on the pavement. When I went over to sniff to see if there was any food around, I discovered that it was not a bundle of clothes but a man looking distinctly sick. He was bleeding from a wound on his head and I licked his hand to see if it was still warm. Having ascertained that it was not a dead body, I set off, determined to ignore The Voice within me which was saying "Do something about it, Tovey".

"I am not going to do anything about it," I said to The Voice as I trotted along. "Someone else will come along, and anyway what do You expect me to do about it?"

I have not mentioned The Voice before because, to be honest, half the time I choose to ignore what it is saying. The Voice generally suggests that I do things which I would prefer not to do. It also speaks the odd word of comfort to me when I am feeling particularly low. When I felt that I would be forever in the Shelter, The Voice told me that things would soon begin to look up. On balance, although I do not often do as The Voice tells me, I like to think The Voice will continue to give me the odd bit of advice and comfort. I was halfway towards the pub when The Voice spoke again.

"Get help, Tovey." I applied my brakes and gave the matter my attention.

Just then a man came out of a side street. It was Charlie. My heart leapt into my throat and I flung myself on him. I have to say that he seemed almost as glad to see me as I was to see him. It was a memorable reunion. He picked me up and hugged me. I could smell his pipe tobacco and his after-shave lotion, and I could feel the roughness of his guernsey under his jacket.

"Come on, the lads will be really pleased to see you," he said putting me down. I was beside myself with joy, but suddenly The Voice spoke. "What about the man?"

I groaned aloud and Charlie stopped. I barked frantically and I stood in front of him, trying desperately to tell him that there was a problem. He stopped and looked at me.

"What's up, Tovey?" he asked, stopping to light his pipe. It was a windy night and as he cupped his hand round the pipe bowl I felt a genuine upsurge of love flow from me to him. I circled round him, barking, and when he tried to go forward I stood in his way, growling. Charlie eventually got the message.

"You want me to come with you?" he said. "All right, let's go." We set off back the way I had come and suddenly Charlie saw the heap of clothes on the pavement. He began to run and in a few moments he was kneeling beside the man. "He's hurt bad, Tovey," he said. "You guard him until I get help." I sat down beside the man and licked his face just near to where the blood was beginning to congeal. His eye flickered open and he groaned. Suddenly, inside my head, The Voice spoke. "Keep him warm, Tovey, that'll help."

I wriggled under his coat and lay as close to him as possible. I hoped Charlie would not be too long, for the man seemed to be getting colder rather than warmer. Just then there was the sound of a Plod siren. I peered out from under the man's coat, but it was an ambulance van and the driver and his mate jumped out.

I wriggled out and stood watching as the men gently lifted him up on to a stretcher which they had brought with them and put him in the van. Just then I heard a familiar whistle. It was Charlie waiting at the end of the street for me. I ran as fast as my legs would carry me and together we went to the pub. Charlie told Mabel and the boys about my rescue and later that evening Mabel 'phoned the hospital to see if the man was alive. When he recovered consciousness, she learned, he told them that, when he was lying on the ground, he dreamt that a dog had come along and stayed with him. Apparently he had been knocked down by a hit-and-run driver and if help had not come he would have bled to

death. Charlie bought me three sausage rolls and Mabel gave me a half-pint 'on the house'. I kept catching my tail with excitement because I was so pleased to be back.

Just when I thought everything was absolutely wonderful, the door swung open and an aroma of flea powder pervaded the public bar of the *First and Last*. I looked up from under the table where I had taken shelter and heard Plod Bob speaking to Charlie.

"Tovey's run away again," Plod Bob said. "We've just had a report." Charlie began to tell him about my public-spirited action and Plod Bob listened with interest. Just then a new Plod colleague appeared and, seeing me under the table, said "There's a black dog answering to the description under that table, Bob."

Plod Bob walked over to the table which was concealing me. He bent down, looked straight into my eyes and winked. "That's not Tovey," he said briskly. "Tovey's better looking than that," and to a burst of applause the two Plods left the pub.

That night, under my tarpaulin, I thought of my adventure and just as I was dropping off to sleep to the sound of the waves lapping on the pier, The Voice said "Well done, Tovey". I wagged my tail and fell fast asleep.

Chapter Seven

LONELY HEARTS

The days of freedom following my rescue adventure were times of special delight. It was a lovely summer that year and every day seemed to be gloriously sunny. I spent a good deal of time exploring the litterbins on the beaches. The Takeaway Food industry, which has caused such problems for those who have to keep the streets and countryside clean, has been an absolute godsend for street dogs like me. I would not pretend that a carton containing a portion of half-eaten cold chips is exactly *haute cuisine*, but it fills a space when you are hungry. The bins usually yield a good harvest and I once found a loaf of garlic bread which gave me particular pleasure. Charlie made a derogatory remark about it when I leapt up that night in the pub and gave him a good face-washing. Apparently he is not addicted to second-hand garlic perfume.

On one particularly sunny day, when I was rejoicing in my carefree existence, I found myself involved in a Lonely Hearts encounter. I was down at Vazon beach during the lunch-hour and I noticed a blonde bikini-clad figure lying sunbathing. The bikini gave me a nasty turn because the PB had a similar scanty swimsuit but, just as I was about to run hastily for cover, I saw that the woman was a more recent model and furthermore she was sobbing into the sand. The PB never wept as far as I knew and I thought there was something particularly sad about a beautiful blonde weeping on a beach. I walked over towards her and she stopped weeping and gazed at me sadly.

"Hullo dog, are you lonely too?" she asked. She had a lovely deep musical voice and I felt instantly attracted to her. (Voices are very important to dogs. Angry voices I find very frightening and I was very relieved to find — when I finally settled with She-who-must-be-obeyed — that she had a laughing sort of voice. Even when She is cross with me, I always sense that the laughter is just below the surface and may bubble out at any moment.) The Bikini-Blonde had a singing sort of voice and she stroked my head very gently when I sat down beside her. She appeared to have stopped sobbing for good and turned over to have a little sleep. From where I was lying I could see a man sitting on his towel, looking over in our direction. I imagined that it was not I who was the object of his admiring glances. I stood up and wandered over to have a closer look at him. He was very good-looking for a man and, as he bent down to ruffle my hair, I could sense that he was feeling a bit lonely too. "Come on," he said to me, "you mustn't leave your mistress alone." I was surprised to find myself bound in a close and apparently permanent relationship to the Bikini-Blonde (hereinafter known as the BB).

We sauntered over to her together and I presented him with the perfect opening gambit. "I've brought your dog back," he said. She rolled over and looked up at him.

"He's not my dog, go away," she said which, by any standards, was not the friendliest of responses. However, he was not a man to be easily put off.

"Would you like to come for a swim?" he asked ingratiatingly. "I couldn't help noticing that you seemed a little upset. Perhaps a swim would take your mind off your problems."

"Go away," she said succinctly. "The problem which I have is trying to forget a man who has just gone off with my best friend. At this moment, the very sight of a man makes me feel sick."

I must say that she was a woman who did not take long to put her point of view. He sat down beside her and gently let the sand run through his fingers. "You mustn't judge all men by one no-good example of the species," he said. "Sometimes it's hard to resist the wiles of a determined woman."

She rolled over again, and I could see that she was searching for some way to get rid of him.

"I am finding it hard at this moment in time to resist the temptation to hit a determined man over the head with my beach umbrella," she replied, reaching for a rolled-up parasol by her side. He jumped to his feet and, as he left, he murmured a phrase which I have always thought summed up my own philosophy in life. The words floated on the air as he ran down into the sea.

"Nothing venture, nothing win indeed!" she said, sitting up to watch his fast disappearing figure. We both watched him swimming strongly out to sea. There was a nasty current at that particular beach on an outgoing tide. Suddenly

we heard a shout and saw an arm waving in the distance. There was nobody on the beach except the BB and me.

She jumped to her feet and raced down the beach. I followed barking furiously. She plunged into the sea and in a few moments outswam me. She had a powerful crawl and my dog-paddle was just not in her league. The man appeared to be going down for the third time when she reached him. There was a sort of miniature whirlpool as she got him fixed in an iron grip. Presently they passed me. He was being pulled on his back to the shore and she was swimming strongly. She must have had a life-saving certificate or two hanging on the wall of her sitting-room! The man looked a little under the weather and she rolled him over and hit him smartly on the back. He coughed up some sea-water in an unconvincing sort of way and I lay down near his face to see if he was still in danger. At that moment he winked at me and I recognised an Artful Dodger like myself.

"I'll never be able to thank you for saving my life," he said weakly. "Do you think you could just give me a hand back to my towel?"

The BB put her arm round his waist and they walked slowly back up the beach. When they got to his towel she sat down beside him, so I settled myself on the sand at their feet. Half an hour later they were so engrossed in conversation that I thought they had forgotten me altogether.

"Let's go and have a spot of lunch," he said reaching for his shirt. She nodded her agreement and bent down to give me a pat on the head.

"Do you think we could take the dog?" she said cajolingly. "I think he might be our lucky mascot."

"Of course we'll take him," he replied. "He looks as if he could do with a square meal and, after all, he brought us together."

She nodded and we set off to find a little something for our stomachs' sake. There is nothing like swimming for giving me an appetite and my new-found friends seemed to be feeling peckish too. They found a restaurant where I could be tied up outside and the owner brought me a very generous portion of fish and chips. After lunch I would have stayed with them for the afternoon but they were gazing at each other in such a lovesick way that I realised that the old adage 'Two's-company-three's-a-crowd' might well apply in this instance. Walking back with them along the road, I recognised three of the local surf kings coming towards us. They recognised the BB's new-found friend and greeted him warmly. I decided to go back with the surfers towards the restaurant, hoping that a defecting lucky mascot would not ruin love's young dream.

"John should be getting in practice for the cross-Channel swim, not chatting up a bird," said one of the surfers to his mates. I stopped in my tracks, remembering the drowning act. I wondered how long it would be before the BB discovered that the man she had rescued had swum the Channel last year and only just missed breaking the world record, and was the hot favourite for the fastest time this year, according to the surfers. Ah well, men were deceivers ever, I thought to myself as I made my way back to the restaurant. Perhaps someone would take pity on a hungry dog who had just brought together Two Lonely Hearts.

Chapter Eight

HELL'S ANGEL

If it had not been for the motor cycle accident I might never have landed back in the Shelter and my whole future could have been very different.

I ought to say at once that I have never liked motor cycles. I dislike the noise they make and I find that, as soon as one comes near me, I have an irresistible desire to chase it.

To be honest, there are many other things which I enjoy chasing — horses, tractors, vintage cars and postmen on bicycles to name but a few. Motor bikes, however, top the list and I developed a rather stupid habit in my free-range days of lying in wait for a motor cyclist and then jumping out of a hedge and watching with interest the evasive action which the rider took. Some of them were extraodinarily skilful and others quite frankly proved that they were not fully in control of their machines. In a way I did a public service through jumping out of hedges at them, because it tested them much more thoroughly than any test that they had to undergo for a licence.

I went on motor-cycle hunts on the days when I was bored with my own company. On the day of the accident I was particularly at a loose end because

Charlie and Jack had gone off to Sark for 'a Norgy'. I had heard them discussing it the night before in the *First and Last* and I gathered that, like the Alderney Norgies, it was going to be what Charlie called 'a right rave-up'. I suppose it was because I was feeling a little left out of it that I decided to have some fun myself. I trotted along the main road to the west as it left St Peter Port, and found a useful bank with a protecting hedge which completely concealed me. I had my first cyclist about an hour later and he proved pretty conclusively that he should have had a Top Rider's Award for evasive action. The next one came along about twenty minutes later and, like the first quarry, he displayed considerable skill in handling his bike under very difficult circumstances. The difficult circumstances were created by me jumping off the bank and out of the hedge and landing close to his side. It took a good deal of skill on my part because the jump had to be controlled or I would have knocked him off his saddle.

I suppose I got a little over-confident because, when the third cycle came round the corner, I misjudged the distance. I leapt too far and landed on his pillion. I felt my legs almost buckle with the impact, while the rider was so astonished to find that he had an uninvited passenger that he braked violently and shot over the handlebars, leaving me in sole charge of the machine. Funnily enough, the cycle — which had been going at some speed prior to my arrival — carried on for about twenty feet with me (without either a dog licence or a driving licence) apparently driving the 750cc monster. Of course, with hindsight, I should have jumped off but I was so astonished at the turn of events that I just clung on for grim death. It was unfortunate that a farmer should have chosen that very moment to round the corner with his herd of cows on their way to the milking parlour. Cows are not unintelligent creatures and, faced with a dog

riding a 750cc motorbike, they know exactly what to do. They scattered like ninepins, and the more nervous of them with delicate bowels laid a trail of cow pats in my path. It proved to be a very effective deterrent, for the cycle skidded on the very fresh manure and my short reign as a Hell's Angel was over. I landed upside down at the feet of an astonished farmer and he slipped his stick through my collar and yanked me upright. My ribs were aching, my mouth was bleeding and I was more dazed than when I was concussed by the golf ball.

The motor cyclist came round the corner, wending his way through the cows. He looked a very shaken man. He told the farmer of my amazing leap and for a moment or two he did not seem to be too cross. When he saw his motor cycle, which had lost some of its pristine charm, his tone changed. "Hold on to him" he said grimly, "I'm going to get the police."

I limped along with the farmer behind the cows. When we got to the farmyard he tied me up to the milking parlour door and I awaited the sound of the Plod siren with trepidation. I could not imagine even in my wildest dreams that Plod Bob would overlook this incident. I was right. Plod Bob listened in disbelief to the Motor Cyclist's account of the accident. The farmer corroborated his statement that, at the time of the accident, I was in sole charge of the machine. "I just don't believe it," Plod Bob said, shaking his head. "You mean he came round the corner actually driving the BMW?"

"He was sitting on the seat, looking for all the world as if he were enjoying it," said the farmer showing an inventiveness for which countrymen are not generally well-known. I did *not* enjoy the experience. I was positively rigid with astonishment that such a thing could have happened to me. Plod Bob shook his head and, taking a piece of rope from his pocket, led me off to his car.

I could scarcely walk and I felt sick before the familiar flea-powder perfume

engulfed me. Plod Bob and his colleague, who seemed to rejoice in the unusual name of Primrose, stopped the car several times to let me out. Each time it seemed more difficult for me to get back into the police car. Eventually Plod Primrose noticed that I was limping badly and decided to get out to help me in. It was then that I noticed that the Plod was a Plodess, and she was very gentle with me when she led me into the Shelter.

Dora was glad to see me but appalled by the account of my motor cycling. The vet had to be sent for to examine me and he diagnosed a slipped disc in my back, which was not surprising in all the circumstances.

"He'll have to lie quietly for a week or two," he said to Dora. When I crept into my cell, I thought it was the most welcome news I had heard for a week.

"She won't have him back, you know," Dora said, speaking obviously of the PB. "She's telephoned to say that if he ever comes in again, we have to have him adopted. Mind you, with his reputation, finding a Prospective Adopter for him will not be too easy."

"Perhaps a circus would be interested," said the vet who was packing up his instruments within earshot of my cell. "Not many dogs could handle a 750cc bicycle and ride it through a herd of cows and not harm one."

"I'd have given anything to have seen him," said Sam who had just come on duty and been given a a graphic account of my Hell's Angel role. "I suppose they'll charge him with riding without a helmet, having no licence or insurance, as well as taking the bike without the owner's permission."

Dora giggled and came in with some hot milk for me. I would rather have had a beer after my adventure, but I reckoned it might be some time before the *First and Last* had me as a customer again. Little did I know that I would never again set paw in my favourite drinking place.

Chapter Nine

LOVE AT FIRST SIGHT

On the morning after my motor cycle escapade I was very stiff and my back hurt. I lay for a time in the warm sunshine in my fenced-in run and reviewed my life, wondering what the future held for me. I am not a dog who suffers from depression and I do not honestly think that a psychiatrist would call me an introvert, but there are times when I feel that I need to reform and settle down. On that first morning of my return to the Shelter I felt distinctly gloomy. It was a Black Day in my personal journey through life.

Rusty was not even in the next kennel for he had gone to a Prospective

Adopter. I had overheard Dora telling someone on the telephone that he had gone to a grower who had a vinery in the north of the island. Adoption is not an easy business for matching a dog to a prospective owner can be fairly tricky. Ideally, the two parties should have something in common and I found it difficult to imagine what a man who grew grapes and freesias could have in common with a dog like Rusty, whose only joys in life were eating golf balls and fighting.

Rusty had been gone for a week, and Sam and Dora were beginning to think they had found a soul-mate for him. I am more of a realist and felt it would not be long before a crestfallen Rusty would be returned to base having committed some heinous crime, such as mistaking the grapes for golf balls and polishing off the season's crop.

As I lay there contemplating life in general and my plight in particular, the morning's boredom was enlivened by two holiday boarders coming into our little hotel. One of the interesting facets of kennel life is to observe owners parting with their pets for holiday periods. There is little doubt that the owners have enormous guilt complexes about abandoning their beloved companions while they scamper off to the Algarve or the Bahamas for a jolly holiday. However delectable the kennel, it scarcely compares with a five-star hotel on the Costa Whatever, and their attempts to persuade their pets that they will enjoy their imprisonment usually falls on deaf ears. I had watched many owners coming in with their animals doing their level best to pretend that Touzer or Queenie was going to just love being shut up in a kennel with a wire run for the whole holiday period.

Some owners adopted the stiff-upper-lip attitude and escaped as quickly as possible with the barks of indignation ringing in their ears. Others made the mistake which mothers occasionally make when they have to take a child to school for the first time; instead of going away quickly, they hesitate and hang around, making the parting all the more painful. When Fifi arrived that Black Morning, I could tell that her owner was going to prolong the parting and make it all the harder for the white poodle about whom she was apparently besotted.

"You will give Fifi her choc-drops every night, won't you?" she said to Dora. "Mummy's little girl loves her choccies." Mummy's little girl wagged her little white puff-ball tail at the mention of the choccies and I thumped by curly black one on the ground to show that Mummy's little girl was not the only one who liked choccie-droppies! Not that I had exactly been fed them nightly in my deprived life!

Fifi was put into the kennel next to mine when, just as we were going to have a friendly sniff through the wire netting, there was a sound like a Sherman tank coming through the doors and a Boxer hurtled down the corridor, pulling Sam after him. I had only ever met one Boxer in my life and I thought for a moment that this might be a different one from the chap who had set upon me near the harbour. Alas, it was the same unfriendly blighter and, as he lumbered past my run, he stopped dead in his tracks. With a mighty growl he leapt at the wire netting, and Sam found himself with an eight-stone punch-drunk Boxer attempting to demolish my security fence.

Fortunately Sam had him on a choker chain and I watched the brute's eyes beginning to protrude as Sam tightened his grip. All would have been well in a matter of moments if Dora had not come through the far door, calling out merrily, "Look who's come back!"

Now all dogs entering the main part of the building had to be on leads, but Rusty was such an old lag that he was treated like a Trusty and he used to go straight to the kennel which was his second home. On this occasion he came through the door looking his usual cheerful self, but his whole deameanour changed when he saw the Boxer half way up my wire netting with Sam holding on like grim death.

Rusty is not an intellectual and he does not, as Hercule Poirot would say, use his little grey cells overmuch. He is a street dog who acts instinctively and I have to own his instincts are usually right. He hurtled down the corridor, scarcely touching the ground, launched himself into the air and sank his teeth into the Boxer's rear end. I suppose Rusty's teeth, having been carefully honed on golf balls, were fairly effective weapons and the Boxer (whose name I later discovered was Butch) let out a howl of pain and leapt towards his assailant. Sam, who was still hanging on to the chain, found the tension suddenly eased and he fell over backwards at Dora's feet. Fifi, Mummy's little girl, pressed her nose against her wire fencing and barked with joy at the sight and sound of battle. It is extraordinary how much women and bitches love a fight. I remember the PB glued to all-in wrestling when it was being shown on television, and she would stay up half the night to watch a match. Bitches are much the same, and Fifi was barking incessantly and catching her tail in her excitement as the battle raged.

It was just when I thought that the scene was beginning to resemble throw-out-time at the *First and Last* that Dora intervened. The tide of many battles has been turned by one clever strategist and Dora proved herself to be just such a one. She took a golf ball out of her overall pocket and, with a shout of "Fetch-it-Rusty", threw it into his kennel. Dora slammed the door, helped Sam to his feet and led Butch to the kennel on the other side of Fifi. It was love at first sight as far as Fifi was concerned and while Sam was putting some ointment on Rusty's teeth marks on Butch's bottom, she gazed adoringly through the netting at him. Butch, despite his pain and chagrin, began to drool in the way only boxers can at the sight of food or the thought of love. I realised, for the first time, that love at first sight was possible under the most unpropitious circumstances. The romance of Fifi and Butch, which blossomed during their time in boarding kennels, would make a wonderful Disney operetta, and I may suggest to Andrew Lloyd Webber that he write a musical about their affair. After all, if he could make such a successful musical about cats, he could surely tackle a more interesting subject.

It was good to have Rusty and his golf ball back in the Shelter. He was such a predictable chap, and I was genuinely fond of him. Apparently, he had been sent back into care because he had insisted that the grower's cat should live permanently up a sycamore tree outside the farmhouse. The fire brigade had been summoned three times in the week so that a fireman could mount the hydraulic ladder and rescue Mimsy, the grower's cat. As soon as the firemen had returned to base, Rusty chased the cat back up the tree and, understandably after three cat-rescue missions, the Fire Chief refused to risk his men's life any more for Mimsy. The grower considered building a treehouse for Mimsy but, after he had nearly fallen out of the tree himself, his wife insisted that Rusty be sent back to the Shelter. Apparently she was quite fond of Mimsy, which I suppose was reasonable enough. She was also well-disposed towards her husband whom she did not want to lose through falling to his death from the sycamore tree. Anyway the grower's loss was my gain and, with the Romance blossoming on one side and Rusty chewing away at his golf ball on the other, I found life in the Shelter reasonably sweet. I little knew that within a month of my return, I would be leaving the security of the Shelter and heading for an Unknown Destination and a New Life.

Chapter Ten

THE DAY OF DECISION

The days in the Shelter slipped by uneventfully. The departure of Fifi and Butch was not without its tragic side for Fifi was collected after a fourteen-day holiday and her joy at being reunited with her owner was clouded by her enforced separation from her beloved Butch. As she was led down the corridor she stopped three times as if debating whether life as Mummy's little girl, fed on choccie-droppies to her heart's content, was going to make up for the ending of her holiday romance.

Butch was beside himself with grief. I would never have imagined in my wildest dreams that a chap, capable of such malevolence towards decent dogs like me, could have gone into a decline over an empty-headed choccie-droppie obsessed white poodle. He refused to eat his food and howled at night, keeping the rest of us inmates awake with his love-sick soliloquies. It was fortunate that the man who owned him came back from the Canaries to take him away. I am not too sure if 'going to the Canaries' is rather like 'going to the dogs'! Perhaps it is a lesser form of dissipation. Be that as it may, Butch's departure, like his arrival, ran true to form. He leapt at my security fence *en passant* but Sam was prepared on this occasion and hauled him off without falling flat on his face in the corridor.

The Shelter was quiet after the nights of melancholy singing but Rusty and I, with the other regulars and the odd boarder, kept the staff gainfully employed looking after our needs. One day, just before dinner, Dora came through to our quarters with Sam, and I overheard their conversation with some misgiving.

"She's sending someone to have a look at Tovey. She thinks he might be just what she wants," said Dora as she passed my kennel. My heart missed a beat as I realised that my future was once more in the melting pot.

"Did she ask what he looked like?" asked Sam as he reached into the run for my dish.

"Yes, she did, and I said he looked rather like a Scottie only longer and higher."

"Fair enough," said Sam. "What did she say to that?"

"She said 'How much longer and how much higher?'. I found it difficult to be precise. How would you have described him?"

"Difficult to describe him, really. His coat's the best part of him. Very shiny and I suppose some people would go for these Queen Anne feet. When's the person coming to look him over?"

"Tomorrow," Dora said. "He's over for the day. Apparently he's a neighbour of hers in Jersey."

Now I may look like a rather high, long Scottie and have Queen Anne feet, but I am not stupid and in a flash I realised the dreadful truth that I was about to be deported! Jersey was, it is true, another Channel island but from what I had heard about it from Charlie and the boys it was a very different place from Guernsey.

Every year there was an inter-island football match and when the final was played between Guernsey and Jersey any supporter from the other island walking into the *First and Last* was in danger of being thrown out unceremoniously. I went along to the final with the boys and sadly Guernsey got beaten. Charlie had a very rich flow of encouraging language when it came to cheering on his team and I can remember him standing on the touchline.

"Break their legs, boys," he shouted with a flood of descriptive adjectives suggesting the type of legs which the enemy collectively displayed. When the ball was kicked outside the pitch for safety, Charlie's howl of "Keep it on the island, you mindless idiots" seemed to me to be a bit hard under the circumstances.

I have to admit that the team from Jersey looked very like their Guernsey counterparts to me, but Charlie always referred to them as 'those ignorant Jersey bastards' which led me to believe that they lacked both the educational facilities and the marriage standards which prevailed in Guernsey. All these thoughts flashed through my mind as the truth slowly dawned on me that I might be consigned to that island so despised by Charlie. The prospect was indeed so daunting that I lay awake for some time that night, wondering how I could give the man who was coming to inspect me such a poor impression of me that he would suggest that I was not an ideal companion for Her-in-Jersey. It was while I was considering what tactic to adopt that it occurred to me that the man would have to be a very astute reader of character and a genuine dog lover to take to me at first meeting. I am the sort of dog who grows on you, and I fell asleep comforted by the thought that anyone over from Jersey for the day would be very unlikely indeed to see in me the boon companion for a dogless neighbour.

The Day of Decision dawned and I sat waiting fearfully for the inspection to take place. Halfway through the morning Sam brought the man through the doors at the end of the corridor.

"Is that him?" he said, coming straight over to my enclosure. "I like the look of him." My heart sank and I wondered if I did my slightly manic tail-catching act it would have the effect of putting him off me. I tried it out at great speed.

"He's a clever chap," the man said. "He's exactly what She's looking for." He came into my enclosure and bent down to pat me. I had to stop going round like a black hairy Dervish because I was beginning to get dizzy and it was obviously not having the off-putting effect that I had intended.

"You'll like Her," the man said to me. "Her dog's just died, and there wasn't a dog in the Jersey Shelter."

I sat down and looked at him in astonishment. He was actually the first human being who had uttered more than a greeting to me. Mostly people said monosyllabic things like 'good dog' or 'Walk' or 'Dinner'. The man, whose name I later discovered was Peter, had actually addressed an intelligent sentence directly to me and he came from Jersey! I stood up and went over to him and gave him my left paw. I am left-pawed and the man Peter bent down and shook it solemnly.

"I'll look out for you," he said. "You and She will get on a treat."

There cannot be much wrong with Jersey if chaps like Peter live there, I thought to myself, and my heart began to lift at the thought of the New Chapter in my Personal Pilgrimage which was presently going to unfold.

Chapter Eleven

A NEW LIFE

I slept fairly well on what was to be my last night in Guernsey. Apparently Peter returned to Jersey on the evening boat and must have reported favourably on me which was, on reflection, strange. I am not a handsome dog and the fact that one of my ears sticks up in moments of stress and the other lies down gives me a slightly raffish look. If, as I gathered, Her-in-Jersey was used to having pedigree dogs, I was going to be a bit of a disappointment at first glance. However I comforted myself on that last morning remembering the Morris Dancers who had wanted to take me to Welwyn Garden City. I also thought of Charlie who would, without a doubt, have adopted me if Mrs Charlie had not 'laid down the law'. (Mrs Charlie frequently laid down the law, which seemed to have a diminishing effect on my friend. Certainly after an Alderney Norgy the law must have been laid down fairly harshly, for Charlie was not at the *First and Last* for several evenings.)

During the course of the morning Dora and Sam came through to inspect our quarters and I listened fairly intently as they chatted about my future.

"She's arranged for him to be flown over to Jersey this evening," Sam said. "He's going in a private plane. Her son works for an airline and they will fly him over. We're to have him at the airport at six."

"I'll miss him," Dora said as she tripped over one of Rusty's golf balls. "There's something about the way he looks at me when I'm speaking. It's almost as if he's listening and understanding."

"Now don't start getting fanciful," said Sam. "A dog's a dog, and once we start thinking they have human qualities we're going round the twist. Tovey is just a dog who somehow hasn't had much of a chance in life. I'd like to think he'll settle down over there and it will be a relief to know that if he runs away he won't become a permanent boarder here again."

Dora bent down and patted my head. She was a nice girl and I was glad that she was going to miss me. I wished I could have asked them about the private plane because I knew absolutely nothing about planes. Indeed, it had taken me quite a time to work out their function.

When I lived with the Tax Exiles they were always going to the airport. Sophy and I would sometimes be taken in the Rolls and, when we got to the place where the planes were, one of the Tax Exiles — usually the man — would get out and kiss the other one good-bye and disappear. A few days later we would go back and get him out of the airport. On other occasions we used to go to fetch the Female Tax Exile's mother from the airport and a week or two later we would put her back into it. I know I was only a puppy at the time, but I honestly thought the place was either a hotel or a prison. The prison idea seemed the most likely for, in the case of the Female Tax Exile's mother, her visits were distinctly hair-raising experiences. She was a very large lady and she was highly critical of the male Tax Exile's way of life. She liked men-who-worked-for-a-living and no one, even in their wildest dreams, could accuse him of that. She also liked ordinary food and was appalled by the food at Fort William.

"Where's the pudding?" she used to say lugubriously when the steak or salmon main course was followed by cheese.

"No one eats sweets nowadays, Mother," her daughter would reply.

"I'm not speaking about sweets. I'm speaking about pudding. I like pudding. I like cabinet pudding, bread-and-butter pudding, jam roly-poly and upside-down pudding."

It was at that point that the fight usually began because the Male Tax Exile also liked puddings and the fat would be quickly in the fire and the pudding would be metaphorically thrown across the table. The Tax Exile's mother would then announce that she was going home and in no time at all we would be *en route* for the airport. The journey was frequently undertaken in stony silence. Once at the airport she would storm out of the Rolls and we would not see her again until we went to get her out some weeks later. Because I was only a puppy, I thought it was a prison where They had put her because of the Pudding Row.

Eventually I did discover that the airport was like the harbour and the people who went there boarded planes which took them to Other Places. I discovered this interesting fact on one of my jaunts when, returning from a Motorcycle Hunt, I lay down for a little sleep outside the perimeter fence of the airport and I watched the planes coming and going. I then noticed that the people came through the airport building and actually went up some steps into the planes. It was a moment of rare discovery for me. I had laboured under a misapprehension for many months and suddenly all was clear to me. I also resolved as I lay there in the grass that I would one day have a ride on a plane and, lying in my kennel on my last day in Guernsey, I realised that my dream was about to come true. I could scarcely wait to fly up into the sky and look down on the islands and the sea from a great height. It would be wonderful.

It would have been a wonderful experience if it had not been for Sam's margarine-coated tranquiliser! He came into my kennel with this offering a little while before we set off. I was a fool to swallow it without thinking. I had heard of people who got slipped Mickey Finns and, in the *First and Last*, I had heard reference to spiked drinks. Who would have thought of margarine laced with tranquilliser?

When the moment of departure came, I was already feeling groggy. Sam took me in the van and I slept all the way to the airport. I was met by a very pretty blonde woman, who turned out to be the pilot, and Sam lifted me into the aircraft where a basket awaited me. They shut down the top and I promptly fell asleep. I woke up as we landed and Simon, Her son, carried me out of the plane, undid the basket and I fell flat on my face on the tarmacadam runway.

"He's drunk," Simon said to the pilot. I struggled to my feet, protesting the while. Under the influence of drugs I may have been, but drunk — never! I was always very careful about the beer I drank and I had never come out of the *First and Last* in other than a totally sober state.

I tried to pull myself together, but I was grateful when Simon bent down and scooped me up in his arms and carried me to where my future owner was waiting. Simon's guernsey smelled of tobacco and I felt a lump in my throat as I was reminded of Charlie whom I would never see again. Suddenly I heard a voice.

"Hello, Tovey," She said. "I've been longing to meet you." She had a laughing sort of voice and I opened my eyes and looked at her. First meetings are important and I wagged my tail with pleasure. I would have given her my paw but Simon had that pinioned under his arm, so a formal greeting was out of the question. She had a friend with her in the car so I was put on the back seat where I promptly fell asleep. Halfway to her house I woke up and, putting my front paws on the back of the front seat, I rested my head on my paws and tried to pull myself together.

"I think he's praying," said her friend.

"Him and me both," She said with a laugh. "It's quite a responsibility taking a Bolter into one's home. I hope he'll be happy."

I heard the word 'Bolter' for the first time that evening, and I was so glad that She knew my breed. In a few moments we arrived at Haut de la Vallée where She lives. Situated at the top of the Vallée de Rozel, the cottage was surrounded by a large unfenced garden. It was right on the little road which ran down to the sea, and I realised it had enormous possibilities for cycle hunts and the like. Inside it was cool and welcoming. She showed me my night basket and my day basket which, considering I only ever sat on chairs and beds, were slightly superfluous to my needs. The day basket was in the kitchen and the night basket was outside her bedroom door.

I went straight to bed and, just before falling asleep, I heard The Voice.

"You'll be all right now, Tovey. She'll look after you and you must keep an eye on her." The Voice was so clear that I shot up in my basket and sniffed to see if someone had come in.

"Go to sleep, Tovey, and remember I'm depending on you to look after her," The Voice continued, and I wagged my tail and fell fast asleep dreaming of my new role as Guard and Companion in the future stretching out before me.

Chapter Twelve

I MEET MY MATCH

Before starting to describe my first day at Haut de la Vallée — which proved to be fairly disastrous — I think I ought to describe the dogs who had lived with Her before my arrival. There is no doubt at all that they programmed Her in such a way as to expect a standard which I found difficult to achieve. My immediate predecessor was a dog called Barney, whose picture in water colours hangs in The Granary. He was obviously a handsome chap, and almost without fault as far as I have been able to gather. My knowledge of her previous dogs comes from listening to the stories She tells children and adults, and from the stories She writes and reads aloud to me when there is no one else about. Of course, she does not realise that I am listening intently and growing more conscious by the minute of my inability to live up to their impossibly priggish standards.

Barney was not the first Barney she had possessed. Her very first dog was given to her by her husband who was a naval chaplain. Barney was a Cairn terrier. He was renowned as a fighter of some distinction. All Scots are bellicose, but Barney was a 'bonny fechter', to use the vernacular. Apparently he once made two Alsatians flee for their lives as he pursued them, attacking them from beneath in what every dog knows to be a thoroughly ungentlemanly manner.

Why then, I found myself wondering, was Barney the First held in such esteem? Evidently his prime virtue was faithfulness, for when Barney was only about two years old, the Padre found himself posted to Malta and it was necessary for Barney to be left with some friends for the duration of that commission. He settled in happily enough in the village where they lived and he befriended an elderly gentleman who lived next door. He spent the days with the old chap and the nights with the friends. The old chap fed him sausages and Barney, knowing on which side his sausages were buttered, seldom left him except to engage in some battle in the village street. The only time he showed he was fretting was when a car of similar make to the one the Padre owned came down the village street. Then he emerged like a bullet from a gun (if a rough-haired Cairn terrier could ever be so described), and he would hurl himself at the car. He was a very proficient car-spotter and never mistook one model for another. For three years he kept up his vigil. Eating sausages and car-spotting made the long days pass more quickly for him. Eventually his patience was rewarded. Three years had passed before the Padre's car came down the village street and Barney the First had the sort of reunion of which he had long dreamed. By this time Simon was part of the family and they rented a house opposite the houses owned by their friends and the sausage provider. Barney refused to pay a social visit to those who had cared for him. He had to be put on his leash to visit the sausage man, and from that time on he followed the Padre like a small brown shadow.

This complicated the naval chaplain's life but he accepted the devotion, realising that Barney was afraid of being left for another three-year stint. Barney went to naval chapel every Sunday and attended the service. He went into detention quarters (smuggled in under the Padre's cassock) and listened while the Padre announced the hymns and the football results in quick succession. In those days there were no newspapers in the naval version of the glasshouse and the Padre was very adept at announcing "Hymn 840 followed by Spurs 3, Manchester United 1". He could get most of the results threaded through his service and, except when Barney stuck his head out and caused a chuckle or two, the services were full of reverence and very popular. It was not until the Commander in charge was faced with a considerable number of sailors in detention quarters putting in requests to change their denomination that the Padre's football results trick was uncovered.

The day came when the Padre left the service and came to a civilian appointment in Jersey, and Barney became an island resident. Having been a regular church-goer, he continued the habit and used to follow the Padre into the pulpit every Sunday. In a way, I suppose Barney the First sowed the seeds of a *modus vivendi* which the rest of us inherited. He died of old age eventually, having been a shining example of Godliness on Sundays and an absolute byword as a fighter in the streets of St Helier for the rest of the week.

He was followed by Rory, the West Highland who, according to my informants, taught a whole generation of diners and bridge- players to keep their feet tucked under their chairs when eating or playing cards. Rory, apparently, disliked feet under tables and would lie growling while a meal or game was in progress. If a foot appeared within an inch of his nose, he snarled his disapproval. As She is a keen bridge-player and not averse to the odd meal, there were certain drawbacks in the little white Scot as a companion. However he kept up the church-going tradition and accompanied the Chaplain every Sunday to his services. The death of the Padre was a body blow to the family but She had long been a lay preacher so She carried on his work and Rory followed her up the pulpit steps, watching her feet as She went lest She mistakenly allowed one to pass within an inch of his nose. A tradition begins in just such a manner and thereafter it was decreed that Her dog went to church. Rory did not live to a great age and he was succeeded by Barney the Second who found church-going very much to his liking. He was a handsome King Charles Cavalier Spaniel and did not mind at all sitting by the lectern or mounting the pulpit steps in solemn procession after his Mistress. Had I known of this strange dynasty of holy dogs into which I had involuntarily been translated, I do not know whether I would have ever eaten that maragarine tranquilliser. However, the shock of the first Sunday was as yet only on the near horizon, and I was in ignorance of my new life-style when I woke up on the first morning. She came out of her bedroom and slipped my lead on and walked me round the garden.

"We don't want you bolting on the first day, do we Tovey?" she said gently, and I glanced up at her in disbelief. Her ignorance of my powers as an escapologist who had no equal was obviously complete. As we walked round the very pleasant garden I wondered how she intended to keep me at home.

"I have some friends coming on Saturday to fence the garden," she said, as if reading my thoughts. "It means you will have to be content with the top lawn, which I shall have fenced and a gate fixed and, if one day you decide to stay at home, then we will get rid of the wire netting." I wagged my tail hopefully and resolved to wait and see how high the wire netting would be before considering whether the area of the top lawn would prove enough for my needs.

Later on that first day She had to drive her friend called Betty, who had been staying with her, to the airport. The name puzzled me at first because She was also called Betty which was a little confusing. She took me with them because She was unsure how I would react if left alone at home.

"He might chew things up," she said anxiously. "I had a friend whose dog chewed the Queen Anne feet off a priceless antique table. Speaking of Queen Anne feet," she said with a chuckle, "Tovey has got a perfect pair." I gazed out of the car window. I had heard the remark before and as my feet have done me a treat in my wandering life I was not going to complain about their allocation to me. Having taken Betty to the airport, we then set forth into town because She had to do some shopping.

"You'd better come with me," She said. "I'm not going to risk your doing anything fearful in the car."

I was pleasantly surprised that her car did not make me feel sick and could not imagine what she had in mind. I allowed her to put on the new lead, which She had bought prior to my arrival, and we set off down the town street. It was our first walk together. It was a Sentimental Moment. Just then a familiar smell wafted towards me. Memories of the *First and Last* flooded over me. In a moment I had wrenched the lead from her hand and flew straight as an arrow from a bow into the pub on the corner of the street. Inside it was dark and friendly. There were several potato crisps trampled into the carpet. Three were cheese and onion, and one was bacon-flavoured. There was a half-empty tankard by a man's seat. In a moment I had managed to get a quick drink and had vacuumed up the crisps at the same time.

Just then the doors swung open and She entered.

"Tovey," she said. It was just like the time when Mrs Charlie came into the *First and Last* because Charlie hadn't come straight home after work. I crawled out from under the table and the man whose beer I had half-drunk gave a shout of rage. I rushed towards the doors, but she had not coped with Barney the First, Rory and Barney the Second without learning a trick or two. She stood on my lead as I rushed past and I bit the dust like a wild steer in a Western rodeo when lassooed by an expert cowboy.

There was a strange silence in the pub as we left. I did not know then that She was not a frequenter of the island's hostelries. Indeed, one could go so far as to say She is one of Jersey's well known non-drinkers and the sight of her in the pub must have made the habitues choke on their lagers with stifled mirth. As we walked along the road, I could sense that our relationship was not going to be too easy a one to cement. Just then, on the next street corner, I caught a whiff of the well- loved smell. Instantly her grip on my lead tightened and She glanced down at me.

"Imagine me getting an alcoholic dog from Guernsey. I should have asked Peter to find out if you'd signed the pledge." Her habit of talking aloud to me was quite unusual. I hoped that She was not a little off her trolley. Just then an acquaintance stopped to chat to her.

"What's that?" he asked rudely, looking at me.

"Do you mean what sort of breed is he?" She said quietly. "He's a Bolter. You don't see many of them around. He was bred in Guernsey."

"Sorry, I thought he was a mongrel," the man said apologetically. "No need to apologise," She said sweetly. As we walked on She winked at me.

"Bolters are a very special breed," She said. "Like other breeds they have their problems, but then I enjoy a challenge." I sniffed and presently, tied to a shop door-blind fitting, waited while she did her shopping. As I sat there patiently I wondered if, after all my wanderings, I had really Met My Match. It was a sobering thought and one that was entirely strange to me.

Chapter Thirteen

AND SO TO A BED

The next day She appeared armed with a mallet and two cow- tethering pegs. In Jersey it was the custom to tether cows so that they did not eat too much of the rich grass. Some farmers still tether their cows and this makes it easier for tourists to photograph them because they are stationary objects. The cows also occasionally wear waterproof overcoats which intrigue visitors. The time-honoured answer to why are the cows thus dressed is always the same: "It keeps the water out of the milk," say straight-faced farmers. The real reason is that it keeps the cows' coats silky but that is never offered as an explanation. But I digress from the cow-tether operation which She undertook on my second day as her dog.

She hammered in the two stakes and joined them with a long wire while I watched with interest from the Granary room window. She then attached a piece of rope to a ring which she had placed on the wire. She completed the operation by putting a second ring at the end of the rope with a dog-leash clipped to that ring. She stood back and admired her handiwork and I looked thoughtfully at this running-dog restraint. There was no doubt about her ability with a mallet and I could see that her determination to keep me at home was going to be almost equally matched by my determination to explore this strange island.

She came indoors and put my own lead on, took me out and attached me to the device. I walked slowly along the sweep of the gravel drive and discovered that I had got quite a good area in which I could run up and down and there was the advantage of a reasonable view of the road.

"That'll keep you at home," She said as She went into the garage with the mallet. I went along to examine the cow stakes and saw that She had indeed fixed them in very firmly. The wire was taut and the ring was designed to keep a frisky Jersey in check. She reversed her car out of the garage and came out to have a final word with me.

"I won't be long," She said. It was the first time I had heard her use that expression but it was certainly not going to be the last. She said it on every occasion as She drove out. Sometimes She would be gone for hours! At other times She was not away for more than a short period. It was a most unreliable expression.

On that first morning of the cow-tether device I spent a few moments running up and down before breaking the loop of my lead by a sharp pull. It would be inconvenient running with a trailing lead, but it was the best I could do under the novel circumstances of finding myself treated like a cow. I set off down the inviting little road which, by the smell of it, led to the sea. I had only gone a few yards before I met a dog from the cottage next door. Later on I was to discover that his name was Beaver and he proved to be a very good neighbour and friend. However on my first morning of total freedom for months I had no time for social dalliance, so I indulged in only a cursory greeting before racing down the valley to the sea. It was a chilly morning and there were not many people about so I examined the litter bins with little success and headed up the main road to see if I could get the hang of my bearings.

Rozel is approached by three roads, our little valley lane and two main roads. I took the St Martin's road and on the left-hand side of that road noticed a large house so I wandered into the garden to have a look around. It was quite early in the morning and there didn't seem to be any people about. The door of the house was slightly ajar so I pushed it open and went in. There was a dish of cat food on the floor of the kitchen which the cat had thoughtfully left for me or for some other passing stranger. I polished that off before going upstairs to see if there was anyone about. I pushed open a door quietly and saw that it was a bedroom and the bed was occupied by a woman who was sound asleep. Seeing her lying there made me realise that I was quite tired with my rush down and up to the bay. I hadn't been on a bed since the days when I had lived with the PB. She used to push me off her bed but I always felt that, after the days I endured with her children, a modicum of comfort was no more than I deserved.

There was no smell of children in this house and the woman on the bed was obviously a deep sleeper whose double bed looked most inviting. I climbed in rather carefully and tucked myself under the bedclothes but put my head on the unoccupied pillow so that I could keep a lookout for any intruders. After all, I felt I owed her something under our somewhat intimate circumstances. I suppose I was tired with all the excitement of moving to a strange island because I fell fast asleep. It would have been better for her if I had been awake when she woke up to discover my head on the pillow normally occupied by her husband. As it was she woke up, saw my black head and proceeded to shriek in a most hysterical manner. I was understandably startled, leapt to my feet and rushed out of the room. Unfortunately she had a rather ornate white lace bedspread which caught in my collar. Her description of my flying down the stairs like a bride with a long train enlivened the neighbourhood for days. At the foot of the stairs I met her husband who had evidently been doing something in an outhouse and heard the shrieks.

"Oh my God," he said, so I stopped in my tracks feeling that a small prayer meeting was about to begin. "Who the hell are you?" he said, "and what have you done to my wife?" I believe that in the pub that evening he told his friends that he thought for an awful moment that she had been changed into some sort of black beast, which proves the effect on the brain of television late-night horror films. His wife then appeared at the top of the stairs and suggested to him that he should detach the bedspread from me. He did this somewhat gingerly and was about to bend down to catch me when I escaped through his legs.

I was much refreshed by the little nap and ready for the next adventure. Just then I heard a voice which, if not yet familiar, was very recognisable.

"Tovey, come here at once!" She was standing at the gate looking distinctly miffed. I viewed the avenues of escape, dodged backwards down a little road and found myself in what I later discovered was a camp site. The extraordinary thing about tents with fitted groundsheets is that they are difficult to enter if the entrance vent is zipped up. A tent without a fitted groundsheet presents no problems, but that morning I crawled under one tent after another causing alarm

and consternation in my train. Those campers who scorned beds and slept on the ground were considerably astonished when I crawled under their recumbent bodies from one side of the tent to another. As I emerged from one tent feeling like someone on an army assault course, a man who obviously played prop forward in his rugger team brought me down with a flying tackle. She was standing beside him.

"Thank you," She said quietly. "He's a free-range dog and he has problems."

The man straightened himself up as he handed her the lead. He was obviously out of practice, for that quite simple flying tackle had winded him completely.

"I had a Bolter once," he said nostalgically. "Cost us hundreds of pounds in fencing and in the end we sent him to be trained as a police sniffer dog."

"Did he pass the course?" She asked, obviously wondering if perhaps this might be a future career for me.

"No, the first time they let him off the leash to search a warehouse on his own he found an open door, took a deep breath of fresh air and was never seen again. There are some you can't train."

As She walked me to her car, I could feel that I was not doing too well on my second day as Guard and Companion. We set off again and, as the car swung into the drive, She spoke for the first time to me.

"I'll get a chain lead for you tomorrow," She said cheerfully, "and then we'll see if the tether works. The sniffer course has got to be the last resort."

I sighed deeply as I went to get a drink of water. I certainly did not fancy being sent off to be a Plod sniffer dog. I would, of course, have a head start over every other dog. I could sniff a Plod a mile off. However, the idea of making a career of sniffing for Plods would be a fate worse than death, and one that I must avoid at all costs.

Chapter Fourteen

IN THE HUNT

The chain proved to be a very successful restraint and I clanked up and down between the cow-stakes, sounding like the old-fashioned convict so beloved by cartoonists. All I lacked was the suit with arrows on it. She assured me that it would be no more than a temporary expedient until the fence and gates were constructed but, as She was doing these with volunteer labour, it might take a little time. Journalists and writers do not, on the whole, make good labourers but her volunteers, whom She had cajoled into digging great holes into which six-foot stakes were to be sunk, tackled the digging operation with a will. I believe that the three who did the major share of the digging were unable to type for a week because of the blisters on their hands, but at the end of a long Saturday the Fencing Operation was complete.

David had made the gates and, as he has a dual skill of carpenter and writer, they really enhanced the top lawn. When they had all gone home, She walked me round the fenced area on my chain to show me their handiwork. It was a pity She had not asked me how high I could jump. I felt grieved for the work that had been done, the blisters which had been acquired and the gates which had been so lovingly crafted. All, as far as I was concerned, were to no avail! We went to bed early on the Night of the First Fencing because She had felt unable to put her feet up while her friends were working and She kept getting them long cool drinks and encouraging them with constant praise. By the end of the day She was tired and I felt sorry for her — not because she was tired, but because it had been a day of wasted effort.

The next day was Sunday and She told me that we were going to church. I had naturally never been to Church as the Tax Exiles were Christmas and

Harvest Festival attenders, and the PB never got up on Sundays at all. I am not going to pretend that I found the experience riveting. I enjoyed going down with her to talk to the children, and did not mind at all sleeping in the pulpit while She 'went on'. What I really enjoyed was the singing and the organ.

"Tovey is the only dog I have owned who really enjoys music," has become one of her much-repeated phrases. She is right. I do like music. I like choirs, orchestras and brass bands, but most of all I like organs. So church-going is no hardship for me. I also realised early on in my relationship with Her that She is someone who likes having her own way and, in minor matters, I am more than prepared to fall in with her plans. It is only really on the question of my freedom that we have a major disagreement.

On the Monday following the weekend of fencing and church-going, She went off to play golf. She left me in the newly-fenced area and said as She left, "I won't be long."

The meaningless phrase echoed in the air like a melody from an old song. I explored my enclosure before going off for a little jaunt. There was the granite barbecue which still had a slight smell of kippers. "There's nothing like a barbecued kipper" is another of her expressions which no one ever contradicts. Indeed, there can be nothing like a barbecued kipper except another barbecued kipper when one thinks about it. I licked the grill for a few minutes and got a slight taste of past delight. I tried the gates to see if they were securely fastened and, on discovering that they were tightly shut, I reversed, took a running start and jumped the fence, landing on the lower lawn. In a moment I was trotting along the road looking for an adventure to brighten the hours till She returned. Who would have thought that on that very day I would have become a member of the upper echelon of island society and joined the hunt?

It took me a little while to realise that we were not actually hunting anything, but pursuing a scent. There are no foxes in the Channel Islands so, in order that those who like galloping on horseback after things should not be frustrated, they have a pastime called a drag hunt. This consists of the pack of hounds following a scent which has been previously laid across fields and hedges, over little streams and through thickets stuffed with rabbits. The riders follow in hot pursuit and when I joined them I really felt that I had reached heaven on earth. The pack of hounds took no notice of me because, with their

noses following the scent, they had no time for the usual pleasantries in which we canines indulge. There was no ritual sniffing and leg-lifting. This was serious hound business. The riders were less oblivious to my presence. I have never really liked horses and, in the past, have enjoyed the quick nip at a passing horse in the course of my travels. There was a big black chap who snuffed and snorted at me so I gave him a little nip on his fetlock to put him in his place. The rider did not appreciate it at all because Black Chap shied dangerously. There were a few pointed remarks and impolite requests to go away, couched in huntsman's language, but on the whole those engrossed in the hunt bore the extra dog in the pack with fortitude. I stopped for a little while in a particularly inviting thicket to flush out a rabbit or two but the hounds were so intent upon the false scent that a real quarry was beneath their notice. I caught up with them after a short interval and it was then that I made another misjudgement — rather like my motorcycle incident. I cut through a hedge just as the Black Chap and his rider cleared it. Black Chap reared up, the rider fell off and as the horse came down on his four feet he lashed out and caught me on my muzzle.

My head reeled and for a moment or two I was concussed. The rider picked himself up and with a shout of rage came towards me. It was time for me to leave the hunt. I have an instinct for knowing when my presence is superfluous. I ran across the field and, after a few minor forays to see if there was any food in two dustbins which had been left out, I made my way home.

When I approached the cottage I saw Her car in the drive. A game of golf probably takes less time than it does to chase a false scent. I collapsed in the garage for a few moments to recover my wind and then awaited the reproach that would inevitably come from my jailor.

As it happened She was deflected from her righteous anger by the sight of some blood on the garage floor.

"You've been hunting," She said with more perception than She realised. "What have you had, a rabbit or a rat?"

There was no way that I could tell her that the blood on the garage floor was mine and that my mouth felt as if Black Chap's shoe was imbedded in my gum.

"How did you get out?" She asked, going to look at the fence and gate. I watched her patrol the area with detached interest. In the years which we have shared together, after She has spent hundreds of pounds on fencing, I can honestly say that She has never seen me leave the premises. She sees me come back but She has never seen me leave. This has added piquancy to our relationship because it means that She can never be sure when She goes out that I will be at home on her return. However, I did not feel like going anywhere for a day or two after the hunt because my mouth felt terrible. I was able to eat but only just, and She was so engrossed in adding boulders to the fence that She never noticed my discomfort. Eventually, three days after my encounter with Black Chap, she threw a rubber ball across the sitting-room floor for me to

retrieve. I am not actually a retriever and always assume that if people throw objects away they do not want them brought back. However I am willing to chase what is thrown and then worry it to death. I ran across the sitting-room after the ball and tried to pick it up. The pain was excruciating and I gave a little whimper. She was watching me, got to her feet and came across towards me.

"What's the matter, Tovey?" She asked. I never wished more than at that moment for the gift of speech. Understanding is one thing but not being able to speak is an enormous disadvantage.

"Sit still," She said gently, "let me look at you." She bent down and very gently touched my mouth. If it had been anyone else I would have snarled but She works hard to get our food and, except for her obsession with fencing, She has many good points. Gently she opened my mouth and the truth was revealed. She had now got a dog with a very common tail, Queen Anne feet, one ear which under stress stands up, and with four broken teeth.

I will not dwell on the journey to the Vet's surgery where some major dental work was undertaken. When I came round after the operation I knew the broken bits of teeth were no longer there and my head felt exactly like it did after my margarine-spiked tranquilliser.

We had to go back after a few days for a check-up and I remember the conversation well.

"Will he manage without his top front teeth?" She asked as I stood shaking on the examination table. I had long ago lost my confidence in visits to vets' surgeries and I was not too sure that I would not be given another shot and recover consciousness to find the rest of my choppers had been removed.

"I can't see him with a false upper denture, can you?" the vet replied. Disappointment flooded over me. Charlie had a complete set of false teeth and used to remove them sometimes and grin in a toothless, witless way at strangers in the pub. I would have loved a false set. However, it was not to be and I have to own that no one ever notices that I am somewhat deficient in the upper jaw. Passing the long-dried pool of blood in the garage after the consultation, She stopped to pat my head and ruffle my hair.

"I'm sorry I thought you'd been hunting," She said. I wagged my tail and gave her a toothless grin. She little knew that I had lost four teeth chasing a false scent.

It was an experience which I would not repeat, for it had taught me a valuable lesson. Life sometimes kicks you in the teeth, especially if you are chasing a horse at the time.

Chapter Fifteen

A DEAD DUCK

Time passes quickly at Haut de la Vallée. We are now in the Period of The Third Fencing. The Period of the First Fencing was short-lived. I jumped the four foot fencing with such consummate ease that I was pretty well a free-range dog once more and I have to own that my behaviour left a great deal to be desired.

"The trouble with Tovey is that he is quite irresponsible," she would say to her friends. She is right. I am an irresponsible dog. Other dogs, when they are loose, do not have the adventures befall them which seem to happen to me. Take, for example my life-saving act during the Period of The Second Fencing.

It was a severe winter and a good deal of snow had fallen. It had packed hard on the ground behind the fence which had been raised to six feet. It was comparatively easy to jump the fence with the help of the snow and I set off one day on a little jaunt to see if all was well in the neighbourhood. She had not been able to take me for a walk for a few days because the road outside the cottage was very steep and covered with a sheet of ice. I was a little bored with my enforced inactivity so I really enjoyed my first hours of total freedom.

The countryside was quite changed under the mantle of snow. It covered the fields and the hedges and it was difficult to believe that it was so nearly daffodil time. Outside the cottage there is a field of daffodils and they must have been surprised by the unexpected blanket which nature had provided for them. It was eerily quiet for there was no traffic — our country roads had not been sanded. I had some difficulty in keeping from slipping as I ran along the road but I made the most of my freedom for experience had taught me that She usually noticed my absence even in the midst of her own preoccupation at her desk. Her ability to recapture me was almost as great as my ability to escape!

I was on my way home when I found one of Peter's ducks suffering from hypothermia. Peter, who had come to view me in Guernsey, lived just up the little road and he kept some hens and ducks. I must say his poultry has been a source of anxiety to Her because of my irresponsible behaviour. I do not think I would knowingly harm one of our feathered friends, but if I were enticed into the pen to play a game of Hide-and-Seek, I am not sure what I would do if provoked.

The duck which I found lying by the roadside was obviously on its last legs. There had been a good deal on the radio and television about the effect of excessive cold on elderly people. There had not, it is true, been any mention of hypothermic ducks but then one cannot expect those who run the television and radio stations to cover every eventuality. However, I knew I had to use my initiative and save Peter's duck from the effects of prolonged exposure.

I began by trying to nudge her with my nose to see if she could stand up, but to no avail. Picking the duck up was not easy for he was a very large duck and I am not a very high dog. I succeeded in getting her into my mouth but it would have been easier if he had not chosen that moment to regain

consciousness. She came to just as I raised my head prior to setting off for home and warmth. I can quite understand that those who witnessed the scene of the rescue might have got the wrong end of the stick. How could they have known that I had assumed the role of a St Bernard on a rescue mission? I gathered afterwards that the general consensus of opinion was that I was making off with one of Peter's ducks. Such a plan was very far from my mind. All I knew, having listened to the broadcast warnings, was that I must get the victim to a warm place as quickly as possible.

It was not easy. Not only was the duck now fully conscious but she was flapping her wings in her anxiety. As I staggered down the road, slipping as I went and trying desperately to resist getting airborne followed by a forced landing, Dulcie looked out of the cottage window.

Dulcie is our Depend-upon who keeps us from falling into domestic squalour while She is busy doing Other Things. I suppose, at first glance, what Dulcie saw was a very unusual sight indeed. We resembled an animal with the body of a duck and the undercarriage of a black dog with Queen Anne feet. I had hoped to take the duck straight into the sitting room and lay it down beside the log fire. Alas, my plan was thwarted by Dulcie emerging from the cottage at break-neck speed, closely followed by Guess-Who. The ice on the road stopped them in mid-flight and I stood rooted to the spot watching them executing some very effective ballet steps. When they regained their balance they came more slowly towards me. Dulcie reached me first and grabbed the duck. I was glad to get rid of her for she was heavy and her tedious wing-flapping had all but thwarted my rescue attempt. As she took over the burden the duck gave me a nasty peck *en passant* which showed the ingratitude of the blighter. I doubt if St Bernard himself was ever rewarded by such behaviour.

At the inquest after the event it was generally agreed that had I been intent upon making off with the duck I would have done so. The fact that I stood still and allowed her to be removed without a struggle was a mark in my favour. No one suggested that I had saved the duck's life. Peter had not noticed that he was one duck short when he shut them up for the night. So, denied the warmth of the rest of the poultry, my duck had fallen victim to hypothermia. She recovered totally from her ordeal. It took me a little while to recover from mine.

She took me into the cottage and began with a lecture which seemed to stem from the lines of the hymn "All things bright and beautiful, all creatures great and small". I noticed She stopped short before the verse which contains the memorable line "He made their tiny wings". She gave me a couple of hefty whacks with *The Times* to drive home her lecture. The rolled-up newspaper technique is her favourite deterrent and I normally receive my punishment with the stoicism which I think I ought to display. Mostly my punishment is well-deserved but on that occasion I felt the injustice of it all and vowed that I would never act the part of St Bernard again. I resolved that if I discovered frozen ducks littering the road between Peter's house and our cottage, I would step over them and leave them to their fate. I had been misjudged, maligned and whacked. It was a perfect example of giving a dog a bad name and, if not hanging him, whacking him with *The Times*. It was a Bad Day during the Period of the Second Fencing.

Chapter Sixteen

THE SARK LARK

If I had known about the trip to Sark I would never have gone. It was a hair-raising experience because it was quite a small yacht and I have never been what you might call a keen yachtsdog.

I was being looked after at the time by the son of She Who Must Be Obeyed. She had gone off somewhere and left me with Simon who had arranged to go to Sark with some friends. When I heard one of them ask "What about Tovey?" I was quite pleased to hear him say "He can come too". She usually replies when people ask what about me, "Tovey can stay at home" which may give the impression that I am something of a recluse, a notion far from the truth. I am indeed a very sociable dog and enjoy visiting people and places. She once hurt me deeply by saying that Tovey is just not the sort of dog you take with you if you want to have peace of mind. I am not sure what she meant by that because sometimes she gives me a piece of her mind which is not a pleasant experience.

The journey to Sark, come to think of it, was not a pleasant experience either. In fact it was an absolute nightmare. I have always thought that seagulls were fair game and learned to chase them on the beaches when I was quite small. At one time it was a necessity to drive them off when people came down with bags of food which they proceeded to empty out for the birds. As I was living rough for quite a long time, I used to lie in wait for these people who, paper-bagged, would come to the sea wall. The gulls would swoop down from the sky and I would approach from the landside and I usually got enough to eat before the Paper-bag brigade drove me off.

I hadn't realised that, on the yacht, the gulls would follow us to Sark. Some of them looked fairly familiar to me. The one with the wart on his nose I had never liked and when he appeared and perched on the mast I began to bark furiously. I'm not a big dog but I suppose I did manage to rock the boat a bit. Simon shouted, "Stop it, Tovey!" and the gull flew off. Forgetting that we were mid-channel, I set off in hot pursuit; well, to be more accurate, in cold and very wet pursuit. It was a nasty moment and Simon and his friends threw a rubber ring to me which I thought showed little understanding of the peril that I was in.

"Get back into the boat," Simon shouted, and I shouted back "How the hell can I do that with this rubber ring bouncing about between me and the deck?" I suppose I should mention at this stage that, although I understand every word those people on two legs say, they do not understand a single bark which I utter, so the conversation is always somewhat one-sided. In emergency situations, such as I was then enduring, I would have given my right ear to be able to speak as well as understand human language. At that moment Old Wart Nose circled overhead and landed back on the mast. With a turn which would have been a credit to an Olympic swimmer about to get a gold medal for the fastest crawl, I changed direction and, with a Dog Paddle potentially the envy of any Canine Olympic Games competitor, I swam for the yacht. Simon leaned over the side and grabbed my collar. He hauled me aboard and before you could say 'Jersey potatoes' I hurled myself at the mast where Old Wart Nose was perched and the next moment we were all in the sea. Well, Old Wart Nose was not with us, but

56

Simon and his two friends landed beside the upturned boat with a tremendous splash. One of the friends, whose name was Jones, was warming up a tin of beans at the time and I am glad to say that I managed to get one or two choice specimens before they sank without trace.

There is little point in recalling how we got the boat upright and climbed back aboard. I have to admit that there was what I would call a distinct atmosphere for an hour or two after that.

"You and your blasted dog," Jones said as he wrung the water out of his hair. "He's not the sort of dog you should take on a boat. Come to think of it he's not the sort of dog you should take anywhere."

I slunk away and sat quietly at Simon's feet. The water was dripping down his jeans into his trainers and he was trying in vain to get the worst of the water off his guernsey. He looked down at me, then took the towel and dried my ears.

"I think one would have to be selective about where to take a dog like Tovey. He could be useful if that bird turned nasty," Simon said placatingly. At that moment old Wart Nose did the thing which seagulls and pigeons have always done to people who are beneath them, geographically if not socially. Jones got the full load just as he was bending forward to tie his shoe laces. He shot to his feet and tried to get the worst of the damage out of his hair.

"Get him, Tovey," he shouted and I launched myself through the air. This time the boat stayed afloat but I was once more in the sea. Old Wart Nose circled above me, laughing uproariously. From the deck Simon threw a crust of the bread which should have accompanied the beans. Wart Nose dived down and I put on a full spurt. I nearly got him, but more importantly I got the crust of bread and swam with it back to Simon. He hauled me aboard once more and I dropped the crust at his feet.

"You're not a bad dog really," he said, "but for Pete's sake, Jones, don't ask him to go overboard again. After all Sark isn't going to be much fun for him with no bitches to meet." I pricked up my ears then. Could I be hearing aright? Had I endured this appalling crossing and three near-drownings to be taken to the Isle of Dogs?

"The Seigneur only allows spayed bitches on the island and visiting dogs have a thin time of it." Simon continued, "Anyway I want him to look after our gear on board."

I spent most of the weekend sitting on the boat, barking. Jones brought back a can of lager from the pub, opened it and went down below. While he was gone I drank it. Abercrombie, who was doing something with the tiller, watched me with his mouth open as I knocked it back in one go.

"You shouldn't have left it lying around where he could get at it," Simon said in tones of deep dismay when Jones came back and was furious because it was apparently the last can of lager on the boat. "She's almost got him on the wagon, but with a dog like Tovey, one beer and he'll revert to type."

I wagged my tail hopefully but I was really too busy composing a letter to the Court of Animal Rights in Strasbourg to report the Seigneur of Sark who was obviously running an island where sexual discrimination was rife.

The trip to Sark, with Old Wart Nose dive-bombing us and the ban on my going ashore, was not particularly enjoyable, although I discovered that Jones was a dab hand at frying sausages and the return trip was so rough that I was the only one who seemed to have any appetite. If ever I were invited to go again — which I think is fairly unlikely — I would disappear before the boat sailed. I am not a sea dog, and the Sark Lark is best forgotten as far as I am concerned.

Chapter Seventeen

A NEAR-DEATH EXPERIENCE

It wasn't long after my return from Sark that I nearly lost my life and ended my days in a watery grave. It was during the Period of the Third Fencing when the drama occurred. The Third Fencing was undertaken by Her in a final effort to keep me within the bounds of her property and prevent Her having to chase after me frequently in her car. I had been a perfect nuisance to the kennels where She sent me when She went on holiday. It was, by any standards, an ideal holiday home. The buildings consisted of an old farm which had been adapted to boarding kennels. It had the enormous advantage over any other kennels in that the play area was communal. So each day we all emerged from solitary confinement to socialise in the old farm yard. It was enormous fun and I enjoyed Her holiday period much more than I had thought I would but, at the same time, I fretted nightly hoping that She would come back as She had promised. When we both returned home, I missed the companionship which I had enjoyed at the boarding house. Many holiday-makers feel the same on their return from their annual vacation but they do not, on the whole, go back and jump up and down outside the boarding house, begging to be let in.

She informed me of the habits of holiday guests when She came to recover me from the kennels' permimeter fence for the third time during the week of my return. In fact, I was not begging to be let in; I was merely barking to my friends who were unfortunate enough to be still in care. However I could accept that her interpretation, though wrong, was hurtful and, as the kennels were some distance away from our home, it was infuriating for her that She had to keep coming to get me back.

"I've heard of recidivists, who are wrongdoers who keep going back to prison, but I've never heard of a dog who prefers kennels," She said morosely.

Of course I did not prefer the kennels. I merely wanted to jeer at those who were still doing time. It was because of these prison visits that we entered the Period of the Third Fencing.

I have to own that this was her most ambitious project. It was untrue of her to tell people that I had watched the Grand National and then resolved to try and leap the six-foot wire-netting fence. The truth of the matter was that the wire-netting had begun to sag a little and I could clear it easily. We both knew that it was possible to put the sort of rigid netting round the cottage which would have been an ideal prison fence. However, it is an attractive cottage and turning it into a Colditz look-alike was unappealing to her. She compromised by purchasing, at enormous expense, some wood trellis fencing which was open-plan. The squares were six inches by six inches, and my shoulders are seven inches across. I mention these figures because they have some relevance. When She bought the fencing, She took me with her and there was a committee meeting held on the premises. The Garden Shop proprietor assured her that there was no way I could come through one of the squares. A lorry brought the fencing and, before having it professionally erected (again, at enormous cost), She put a piece up in front of the garage door and held it there, blocking the entrance. She is not only an untrusting woman, but quite intelligent too.

She then called me from the other side of the fence and suggested that I try one of my Houdini tricks. First of all I put one paw through the aperture and then withdrew it. Then I put my head through and withdrew that. Finally I put one shoulder, one paw and my head through the hole and eased my body through and came out on the other side. As I looked up at her for a commendation, She was swaying slightly on her feet.

"I don't believe it," She said so faintly that I thought She might actually pass out. "It will be necesary to fix the wire netting to the trellis at the top and sink it at the bottom."

That is the current position in the Period of the Third Fencing. I sometimes take a flying leap, scramble up the netting and slip through a hole at the top, but it is painful and frankly I only do it in an emergency. I am no longer sent to the kennels when She goes away. Mary has me. Mary is a friend and she loves me. She sits at the piano sometimes and sings *Rose of England*. She sings other songs too, but that is my favourite. I have a lady friend called Rose who happens to be an English setter. She is really rather an aristocratic dog but we are firm friends. When Mary sings *Rose of England*, I think of her and look soulful which does not pass unnoticed. Mary usually gives me a small piece of milk chocolate when I look soulful, which is nice. I like staying with her very much and her garden is, as She says, Tovey-proof. I don't think they miss me at the kennels because I was a Disruptive Influence and my subsequent calls on the place were not popular.

It was not long after the erection of the trellis fencing that She nearly lost me altogether. We had been invited out for tea with some friends who live at the other side of the island. It was a heavenly day and one that stands out in my mind. During the course of the afternoon it was suggested that She might like a sail across the bay. The Sark Lark was still fresh in my mind, so I was glad to hear that the remainder of the party would look after me on the beach.

I don't know when I began to get panic-stricken. I watched quite happily as the yacht left the shore after She had waded out to board it. I ran up and down the water's edge barking as the wind billowed out the sails and the boat set off

across the bay. It was when it turned to go out to the open sea that I panicked. She had become very important to me. She was my lifeline and, although I was a trouble to her, She genuinely loved me and I was, and am, devoted to her. Sometimes in the winter evenings when I am sound asleep in my day basket which is carried from the kitchen to the sitting-room, she looks up from her book and says, "Give me a kiss, Tovey". I pretend not to hear at first but when She persists I climb reluctantly out of my bed, walk over and lick her hand. I then walk back to bed in a stiff-legged way to indicate my displeasure at being wakened up for such a trivial reason. "I've never seen a dog who demonstrates so precisely the male reaction to a demand for affection at an inconvenient time. He personifies reluctance tinged with acquiescence," She said once to a guest who was staying with us and who had witnessed the evening routine.

I mention that as an example of the feminine misconception of the male outlook. When one is sound asleep, having to drag oneself across the room to prove one loves someone is unreasonable. My devotion to her is very real and I was thinking about how I would feel if anything happened to her, when the yacht began to head out to sea. So with no thought for my personal safety I plunged into the sea and started swimming after the yacht.

There was quite a nasty current flowing and I was buffeted by the off-shore waves. I am not a long-distance swimmer but manage with my dog paddle to keep up quite a reasonable speed. No one on the beach noticed my defection. Those on the yacht were too far away to see my black head bobbing up and down in their wake. Gradually the awful truth dawned on me. I had reached the point of no return. I was tiring and not gaining on the yacht. I had swum too far out to return and my legs were beginning to ache. I felt I just could not go on.

I began to swallow a good deal of water and as I floundered in the sea the waves seemed to grow bigger. Just then I heard a shout from the shore and I noticed the yacht begin to turn about.

"I'm coming, Tovey," Her voice came across the bay. I hoped she would be in time. My heart was thudding and I felt I could not swim another stroke.

"You've got to hold on," another voice said. This time it was The Voice which, during my life, has given me encouragement and advice. "I'll still the waves, you keep swimming."

Suddenly the water seemed calmer and I stopped swallowing water. I felt reassured and stopped thrashing about. In no time at all the yacht was alongside me and She was helping to pull me aboard. I lay in the bottom of the boat gasping like a stranded fish. She put her hand on my head and there was no reproach, no threat of a whacking with *The Times*.

When we got back to the beach, I shook myself dry but stayed close to her. I had been a Very Worried Dog!

"Funny how the wind changed direction," said Paul, who owned the yacht. "It was blowing offshore and then suddenly the wind was in our direction."

On the way home in the car I thought about my adventure and my life with her. It had been a Grim Page in my Personal Pilgrimage. I had some supper and, because I was very tired, fell sound asleep in my basket. She was working at her desk when through the mists of sleep I heard her speak.

"Give me a kiss, Tovey."

I sighed deeply, shook myself awake and staggered over to where she was sitting. I licked her hand and dragged myself back to my basket. One would have thought that after I had nearly lost my life to show my devotion to her, She would have been satisfied without having to rouse me from my much-needed sleep for a tender moment! As I dropped off to sleep for the second time I thought that being Guard and Companion has disadvantages as well as benefits, but I wouldn't change places with any dog in the land, not even with a Corgi at You-know-where.

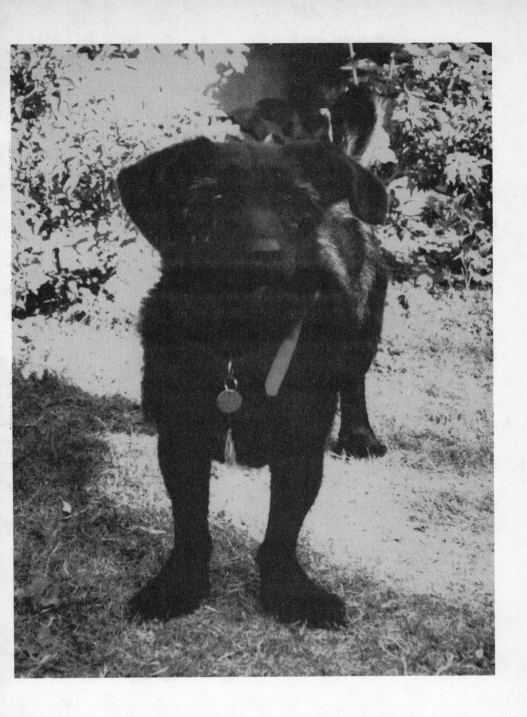

Tovey . . . with the famous Queen Anne legs.